£2

ELIM CHORUSES
BOOKS 1-18

Compiled by

W. G. Hathaway

VICTORY PRESS

EASTBOURNE

First printed in one volume 1966

COPYRIGHT

**Most of the choruses contained in this book are copyright
and may not be reprinted without written permission.**

Printed in Great Britain
for Victory Press (Evangelical Publishers Ltd.)
Lottbridge Drove, Eastbourne, Sussex,
by Compton Printing Ltd. London and Aylesbury

INDEX TO FIRST LINES

Elim Choruses, No. 1

1   He Keeps Me Singing

L. B. B.

L. B. Bridgers.

Je - sus, Je - sus, Je - sus,— Sweet-est name I know,

Fills my ev - 'ry long - ing, Keeps me singing as I go.

2   Jesus, First Thought in the Morning

J. J. C.

J. J. Culley.

Jesus, first thought in the morn - ing! Jesus, the last thought at night!

Je - sus, my song All the day long, Keeping me happy and bright!

3 All Things in Jesus

H.D.L.

H. D. Loes.

All that I want is in Je - - sus, He sat - is -
Je - sus, in Je - sus,

fies..... joy He sup-plies; Life would be worth-less with-
with the   free-ly   with-

ad lib.

out   Him, All things in Je - sus I find. ....
out Him, with-out Him,

4 He's the Lily of the Valley

Slowly, with expression.

Arr. by W. G. Hathaway.

He's the Li - ly of the Val - ley to my soul,
He's the Al - to - ge - ther Love-ly to my soul,

He's the Lil - ly of the Val - ley to my soul.
He's the Al - to - ge - ther Love-ly to my soul.

5 The Grand Old Book

The grand old Book, the grand old Book, You'll find the words of com-fort where-ev-er you may look, In sor-row or in pain, His prom-is-es are plain, So keep on be-lieving in the grand old Book.

6 God Has Blotted Them Out

Words and Music by Mr. and Mrs. Seth Sykes.

God has blot-ted them out, God has blot-ted them out, My sins like a cloud hung o-ver me, He blotted them out when He set me free, God has blot-ted them out, God has blot-ted them out.

7 Some Day I Shall Be Like Him

J.L.H.

J. Lincoln Hall.

Some-day I shall be like Him, Some - day, like Him;

1st time.

Chang'd in - to hea-ven-ly beau - ty, When His face I see;

2nd time.

Hal - le - lu - jah! This wonderful promise, He gives to me. . . .

gives to me.

8 Running Over

Seth Sykes.

W. Gardner Hunter.

Run - - ning o - ver, Run - - ning o - ver, My cup's

My cup's running o - ver, My cup's running o - ver, Glo - ry! my cup's

filled and run - ning o - - ver, Since the Lord sav'd me, I'm as

Since the Lord sav'd me,

hap - py as can be, My cup's filled and run-ning o - - ver.

9

Is it the Crowning Day?

George W. Whitcomb.

Chas. H. Marsh.

Glad day! Glad day! Is it the crown-ing day? I'll
live for to-day, nor anx-ious be, Je-sus, my Lord, I soon shall see;
Glad day! Glad day! Is it the crown-ing day?

10

Tell the World

W.G.H.

W. G. Hathaway.

Tell the world that you have found a pre-cious Sa - viour! Tell the
world that there is healing in His Name! Let them know that He can fill you with His
Spi - rit, But best of all that He is coming back a - gain.

11   In My Heart There Rings a Melody

Mr. and Mrs. S. Sykes.   Harmonised by Mrs. S. Sykes.

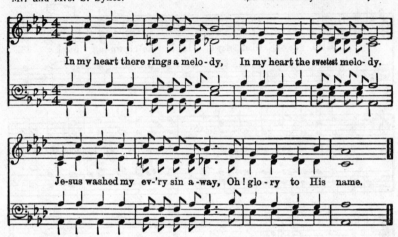

In my heart there rings a melo - dy, In my heart the sweetest melo - dy.

Je-sus washed my ev-'ry sin a-way, Oh! glo - ry to His name.

12   Oh, How I Love Him

Arr. by W. G. Hathaway.

Oh, how I love Him! How I a-dore Him! My Breath, my

Sun - shine, My All in All. The great Cre - a - tor Became my

Sa - viour, And all God's ful - ness Dwell-eth in Him.

Hallelujah !

Arr. by W. G. Hathaway.

Hal -le - lu, hal-le -lu, hal- le -lu, hal- le -lu - jah, praise ye the Lord !

Hal-le - lu -jah, Hal-le -lu-jah, praise, O praise the Lord.

Praise the Lord, hal-le-lu - jah! Praise the Lord, hal -le- lu - jah!

Praise Him, praise Him, Praise Him, praise Him,

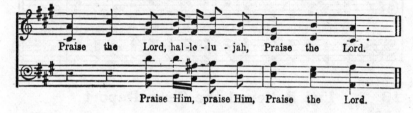
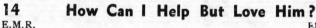

Praise the Lord, hal -le -lu - jah, Praise the Lord.

Praise Him, praise Him, Praise the Lord.

14   How Can I Help But Love Him?

E.M.R.

Elton M. Roth.

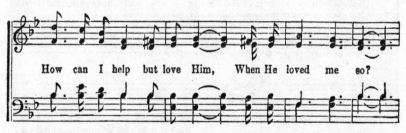

How can I help but love Him, When He loved me so?

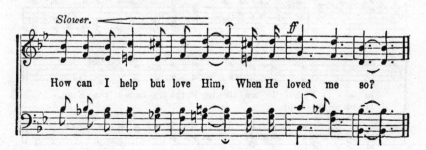

How can I help but love Him, When He loved me so?

Slower.

ff

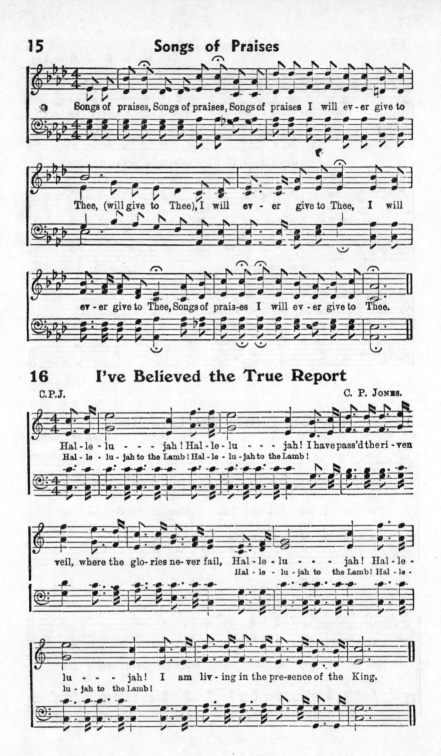

15

Songs of praises, Songs of praises, Songs of praises I will ev-er give to Thee, (will give to Thee), I will ev-er give to Thee, I will ev-er give to Thee, Songs of prais-es I will ev-er give to Thee.

16 I've Believed the True Report

C.P.J.   C. P. Jones.

Hal-le-lu - - - jah! Hal-le-lu - - - jah! I have pass'd the ri - ven
Hal-le-lu-jah to the Lamb! Hal-le-lu-jah to the Lamb!

veil, where the glo-ries ne-ver fail, Hal-le-lu - - - jah! Hal-le-
Hal-le-lu-jah to the Lamb! Hal-le-

lu - - - jah! I am liv-ing in the pre-sence of the King.
lu - jah to the Lamb!

This is Like Heaven

17
J.E.F

J. E. French.

Oh, this is like hea-ven to me (to me), Yes, this is like
Oh, that will be hea-ven to me (to me), Yes, that will be

hea-ven to me (to me): I've cross'd o-ver Jor-dan to
hea-ven to me (to me): A cloud of bright an-gels to

Can-aan's fair land, And this is like hea-ven to me (to me).
car-ry me home, Yes, that will be hea-ven to me (to me).

That Convention in the Air

18
T.H

Thoro Harris (arr.).

That Con-vention in the air! How I'm long-ing to be there, When the

saints from ev-'ry land shall meet. Christ Himself will there preside, With His

loved ones, glori-fied, Who will wor-ship at His sa-cred feet.

19 His Face Will Outshine

T.H.

Thoro Harris.

His face will outshine them all, His face will outshine them all;

Glo-ry to the Lamb, Halle - lu - jah! His face will outshine them all.

My Saviour's face

20 Lest I Forget Gethsemane

J. E. Hussey.

Wm. J. Kirkpatrick.

Lest I forget Geth-sem - a - ne, Lest I for-get Thine a-go-ny,

Lest I for-get Thy love for me, Lead me to Cal-va - ry.

Copyright 1921, by Hall Mack Co. International Copyright secured.

21 Wonderful Treasure

W.G.H.

H. Palmer.

All my sins are for-giv - en, Through the Side that was riv - en;

Pow'r from heaven is giv - en, Christ Je-sus for me.

Speak, My Lord

G.B.

George Bennard.

Speak, my Lord, speak to me, Speak, and I'll be
Speak, my Lord, speak to me,

quick to an-swer Thee; Speak, my Lord, speak to
to an-swer Thee; Speak, my Lord,

rit.

me, Speak, and I will answer, "Lord, send me."
"Lord, send me.

23 I Love Him Better

I love Him bet-ter ev-'ry day, I love Him bet-ter ev-'ry day;
I have the glo-ry in my soul, I have the glo-ry in my soul.

Close by His side I will a-bide, I love Him bet-ter ev-'ry day.
I feel its pow'r this ve-ry hour, I have the glo-ry in my soul.

I Love my Jesus

MRS. CHAS. SHREVE.

I love my Je - sus, for He's my Sa - viour, And He has brought me un to the foun - tain, The blessed foun - tain of liv - ing wa - ter, The cry-stal foun-tain that ne-ver shall run dry. . . . . . .

ne - ver shall run dry.

Sweeter as the Days Go By

Mrs. C. H. M.

Mrs. C. H. Morris.

Sweeter as the days go by, . . Sweeter as the days go by;
Sweet - er as the days go by, 'Tis sweet - er as the days go by;

Rich - er, full - er, deep - er, Je-sus' love is sweeter, Sweet-er as the days go by.

I am Free !

I am free! I am free! Je-sus Christ has paid my debt on Cal-va-
Long a - go, long a - go, Yes, the old account was set-tled long a-

ry, And the bless-ed Ho-ly Ghost, In my heart is now the
go, And the re-cord's clear to-day, Je - sus wash'd my sins a-

Host, Hal - le - lu - jah! Bless-ed Sa - viour, I am free!
way, For the old ac - count was set - tled long a - go.

27 In My Heart there Rings a Melody

E.M.R.   Elton M. Roth.

In my heart there rings a me - lo-dy, There rings a me - lo-

dy with hea-ven's har - mo -ny; In my heart there

rings a me - lo-dy; There rings a me - lo-dy of love. . . .

I'm Acquainted with the Author

Words and Music by Mr. and Mrs. Seth Sykes.

I'm ac-quainted with the Au-thor, And I know God's Word is true; In times of grief it brings re-lief, And tells me what to do. How I dear-ly love its pa-ges, For I've found the 'Rock of A-ges,' I'm ac-quaint-ed with the Au-thor, And I know it's true.

29   Mine! Mine! Mine!

Anna Hudson.

R. Frank Lehman.

Mine! mine! mine! I know Thou art mine;

Sa - viour, dear Sa - viour, I know Thou art mine.

30 Wonderful Name !

R. E. Darragh.

L. Prentice.

Name, Name, won-der-ful Name,—Je - sus, Je - sus, Je - sus!

Name, Name, glo - ri - ous Name,—Precious Name of Je - sus!

31 Come and Dine

C. B. Widmeyer.

"Come and dine," the Master calleth, "Come and dine;" You may feast at

O ccme and dine:

Je - sus' ta - ble all the time; He who fed the mul - ti-

O come and dine,

tude, Turned the wa - ter in - to wine, To the hungry calleth now, "Come and dine."

Love, Wonderful Love

Mr. and Mrs. Seth Sykes.

Love wonder-ful love, The love of God to me.

Love, O the wonder-ful, wonderful love, The love of God to e-ven me.

Love, won-der-ful love, So great, so rich, so free;

Love, O the wonder-ful, wonderful love, So great, so boundless and so free.

Wide as wide as the o-cean, Deep, as deep as the sea, . . .

Wide as wide as the o-cean, Deep, as deep, Deep as the deepest sea,

High, as high as the heav'ns a--bove, His love to me.

33   Just the Same

W. H. Jude.

Just the same, . . Just the same, . . God is just the same to-day, . .

Just the Same (*Continued*)

Just the same, .. Just the same, .. God is just the same to - day. ....

34 Rolled Away

Arr. by W. G. Hathaway.

Roll'd a-way, roll'd a-way, roll'd a-way, And the burden of my heart roll'd a-

Rolled a - way Roll'd away,

way; Roll'd a - way, roll'd a-way, roll'd a - way, And the

Roll'd a way, roll'd a - way,

bur-den of my heart roll'd a - way, Ev - 'ry sin had to

Ev -'ry sin had to

go 'neath the cleans - ing flow, Roll'd a - way, roll'd a

'neath the cleansing flow, Roll'd away,

way, And the bur - den of my heart roll'd a - way.

He's Everything to Me

He's ev-'rything to me, ... From sin He sets me free; .. His
He's all to me, He sets me free;

peace and love my por-tion through all e-ter-ni-ty! He's
e-ter-ni-ty!

ev-'ry-thing to me, ... More than I dream'd could be; .... O
He's all to me, could be;

praise His name for ev-er, He's ev-'ry-thing to me.

He's the One I Love

Words and Music by a Clergyman.

He's the One I love at morning, He's the One I love at noon—He's the One at ev'ning

He's the One I Love (Continued)

twilight, He's the One at midnight gloom; He's the Oak and I'm the i - vy, He's the

Potter, I'm the clay—And for Him and me there'll never come a part-ing day.

37   Let the Beauty of Jesus

Albert Orsborn.   Arr. by Tom Jones.

Let the beau-ty of Je-sus be seen in me, ...

All His wonderful passion and pu - ri - ty; . . . .

O Thou Spi-rit Di -vine, all my na-ture re -fine,

Till the beau-ty of Je-sus be seen in me. . . . .

Let's Go

H. Buffum, arr. by W. Rogers.

Let's go, (let's go,) let's go, (let's go) To the land where milk and honey flow; Let's go, (let's go,) let's go, (let's go,) Where the grapes of Es- chol grow. Let's go, (A-men.) Let's go, (let's go,) We can well possess the land, I know; With a bounding heart we'll make the start, All a - board, let's go.
(All a -board,) (let's go.)

---

39   The Hallelujah Meeting

J. R. Cupples.   Harmonised by W. Hicks.

Oh! yes, I'll be there! hal-le - lu -lah; I'll be there, At the hal- le-lu- jah

meet-ing o - ver there; And I'll shout hal - le - lu - jah when I

see my Saviour there, At the hal - le - lu - jah meeting o - ver there (over there).

40 ## Midnight to Midday for Me

Words and Music by Mr. and Mrs. Seth Sykes.

Mid-day was turn'd to mid-night, When Je-sus died on the tree;

Mid-day was turn'd to mid-night, when Je-sus suffer'd for me.

I so unworthy and help-less, He made mine eyes to see;

Glo - ri - ous light, sunshine so bright—Mid-night to mid-day for me.

41 The Promised Pentecost

D.W.M.

D. W. Myland.

I am glad the prom-ised pen-te-cost has come, And the
Lat-ter Rain is fall-ing now on some. Pour it out in floods, Lord,
on the parchèd ground, Till it reach-es all the earth a - round.

42 I Know I Owe

Old Melody.

Arr. by W. G. Hathaway.

I know I owe, I know I owe A debt of
I know I owe, I know I owe,

love to Him I know I owe— Back to my sin I dare not
A debt of love to Him I owe— Back to my sin

go Be-cause a debt of love I owe.
I dare not go Be-cause a debt of love I know I owe.

I Have an Interest

Arr. by W. G. Hathaway.

I have an int'rest in the Bleeding Lamb, I have an in'trest in the Bleeding Lamb,

I have an int'rest in the Bleeding Lamb, the Lamb of Cal - va - ry.

44

Let's Go On

Arr. by W. G. Hathaway.

Let's go on, Let's go on! talk- ing a - bout this good old way,

Let's go on, lets go on! talk- ing a - bout the Lord:

I feel so much bet- ter, talk - ing a - bout this good old way,

I feel so much bet-ter, talk - ing a - bout the Lord.

'Twas a Glad Day

A.S.R.

Albert S. Reitz.

'Twas a glad day when Jesus found me, When His strong arms were thrown a-
round me, When my sins He bu-ried in the deep-est sea, And my
soul He fill'd with joy and vic-to-ry, 'Twas a glad day, O hal-le-
lu - jah! 'Twas a glad day He claim'd His own; I will shout a
glad ho - san-na in glo-ry When I see Him up-on His throne.

46 Let All the People Praise Thee

Mrs. C. H. M.

Mrs. C. H. Morris.

Let all .... the peo-ple praise Thee Let all ... the peo-ple
let all   let all

Let All the People Praise Thee (Continued)

praise thee! Let all ..... the peo-ple praise Thy name for-
let all

ev-er and for-ev-er-more for-ev-er-more, O Lord! Let more.

47   **Victory Chorus**

W.R.   W. Rogers.

Marching in cho-rus, Je-sus be-fore us, Four-square Gospel workers are we,

Tho' men may taunt us, Nothing will daunt us, on-ward to vic-to-ry.

Je-sus the Sa-viour, Je-sus the Heal-er, Bap-tis-er, com-ing King!

Small notes for repeat.

Ev-er is near us, rea-dy to cheer us; on then and let us sing!

Jesus, My All in All

D.B.G.

Douglas B. Gray.

Je - sus, He is my All in All, Je - sus, He is my All in All;

In cloud or sunshine He's the same, Oh! Hal-le-lu - jah, Praise His Name!

What - e'er the future has in store, I know that He will go be-fore,

Guiding and keeping me from harm, For He's my All in All.

49

I'm on My Way

Arr. by W. G. Hathaway.

I'm on my way to Glo-ry Land, I'm on my

I'm on my way to Glo-ry Land,

way   to Glo-ry Land,   I'm on my way   to Glo-ry

I'm on my way   to Glory Land,   I'm on my way

Land,   I'm on my way, praise the Lord, to Glo-ry Land.

to Glo-ry Land,

50   Oh, I Love Him

Oh! I love Him! Yes I love Him, Since for me He bled and died,

Oh! I love Him, Yes I love Him, More than all the world be-side.

51   Holy Ghost, We Bid Thee Welcome

Mrs. C. H. M.   Mrs. C. H. Morris.

Wel-come, wel-come   wel-come,   Ho-ly Ghost, we welcome Thee;
Holy Ghost we bid Thee welcome, bid Thee welcome, Blessed Holy Ghost, we wel-come Thee;

Come in power and fill   the tem-ple, Ho-ly Ghost, we wel-come Thee.

I Ain't a-Go'n a Grieve

Negro Melody.

Arr. by W. G. Hathaway.

1. My pre-cious Lord . . . . has won my heart . . . . And ne-ver
2. O see that sun . . . . see how she run . . . Don't ever let her
3. You may talk about me . . . as much as you please, . . . I'll talk about
4. Then some fine morn - - - ing bright and fair, . . . I'll don my

My precious Lord   has won my heart

from . . . . Him will I part; . . . . My pre-cious
catch you . . . with your work un-done; . . . . . O see that
you . . . . down on my knees; . . . . You may talk about
wings . . . . and try the air; . . . . . . Then some fine

And ne-ver from   Him will I part;

Lord has won my heart and ne-ver from Him will I part; I aint a gon a
sun, see how she run, Don't ever let her catch you with your work un-done; I aint a gon a
mess much as you please, I'll talk about you down on my knees; I aint a gon a
morning bright and fair, I'll don my wings and try the air; I aint a gon a

REFRAIN.

grieve . . . . my Lord a-ny more. . . . . I aint a gon a
I aint a gon a grieve   my Lord a-ny more.

grieve my Lord a-ny more, I aint a gon a grieve my Lord a-ny more, I aint a gon a

I Ain't a-Go'n a Grieve (Continued)

REFRAIN. *Slower.*
after last vrs. only

grieve . . . . my Lord a-ny more. I aint a gon a

I aint a gon a grieve   my Lord a-ny more.

grieve,   I aint a gon a   grieve,   I aint a gon a

I aint a gon a grieve,   I aint a gon a grieve,

rit.

grieve   my Lord a-ny   more. . . . .

I aint a gon a grieve   my Lord a-ny more.

53   Yes, I Know

Mrs. A. W. W.   Mrs. A. W. Waterman (arr.).

Yes I   know, ... I sure-ly   know, ... Je-su's

Yes I   know,   I sure-ly know,

blood can make the vi-lest sinner clean. Yes I   know, ... I sure-ly

Yes I know,   I

know . . .   Je-su's blood can make the vi-lest sin-ner clean.

surely know.

Calvary (Continued)

ry . . . . is the place where my blind eyes were o - - pen'd,—

Je - - sus my Sa - - viour became pre - cious to me.

56 I've Moved

Rev. James Bruce MacKay.   J. Lincoln Hall.

I've moved, I've moved, O - ver in-to Ca-naan land; I've
I've moved, I've moved,

moved, I've moved, O-ver in-to Canaan, land of milk and honey;
I've moved, I've moved,

I've moved, I've moved, O-ver in-to Ca-naan land, Where
I've moved, I've moved, (I've

love and peace abound, And no carnal thing is found, I've moved, I've moved.
left the land of Doubt, And I'm in the land of Shout,) I've moved, I've moved.

Hallelujah, Amen

J. Fawcett.

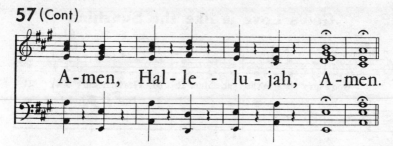

A-men, Hal - le - lu - jah, A - men.

Elim Choruses, No. 2

58   **He is Mine, Jesus the Saviour**

Inscribed to Evangelist R. E. Darragh.

SETH SYKES.   MR. & MRS. S. SYKES.

He is Mine! .. He is Mine! ..

Jesus the Saviour who died for me, Purchas'd my pardon on Cal - va-ry;

He is Mine! .. He is Mine! ... There's

nothing can sev - er for I'm His for ev - er, He is Mine! ..

59   God's Love is like the Sunshine

Arr. by W. G. HATHAWAY.

God's love is like the sun-shine, It co-vers land and sea; It fills my heart with glad-ness When I know that God loves me.

60   Let Glasgow Flourish

G.T.F.

MR. & MRS. SETH SYKES.

'Let Glasgow flourish By the preaching of the Word, And the praising of His Name,' This
(His Name,)

glo-rious motto ev-er keep in view, It saves from sin and shame, All
(and shame,)

those who love and follow Christ the Lord, This message shall pro-claim; 'Let
(proclaim;)

The first line of this chorus is actually the motto of the city of Glasgow. The name of
any other town may be sung in place of Glasgow.

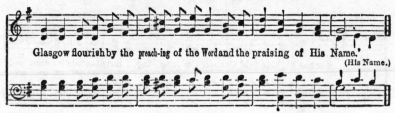

Glasgow flourish by the preach-ing of the Word and the praising of His Name.

(His Name.)

61   Blotted Out!

Arr. by W. G. HATHAWAY.

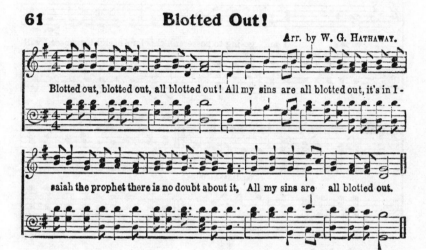

Blotted out, blotted out, all blotted out! All my sins are all blotted out, it's in I-

saiah the prophet there is no doubt about it, All my sins are all blotted out.

62   I lost it on Calvary's Hill

Arr. by W. G. HATHAWAY.

I lost it on Calva-ry's Hill; It tumbled and tumbled un-til It

roll'd out of sight, I was happy that night, I lost it on Cal-va-ry's Hill.

The Highlands of Canaan

H.L.

HALDOR LILLENAS.

For the highlands of Canaan I'm long-ing, I have tasted its corn and wine; (its corn and wine;) I am go-ing to possess all this land of righteousness, I will claim it and make it mine. (and make it mine.) I have left the desert sand for the blessed Beulah land, Hal-le-lu-jah for ev-er-more!

64   God is Love!

G.T.F.

MR. & MRS. SETH SYKES.

God is Love! I feel it in the air a-round me, God is Love! I

God is Love (Continued)

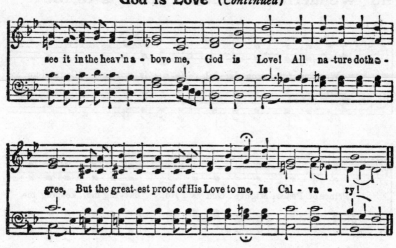

see it in the heav'n a - bove me, God is Love! All na -ture doth a -

gree, But the great-est proof of His Love to me, Is Cal - va - ry!

65 His Name shall be Jesus

MRS. C. H. M.   MRS. C. H. MORRIS.

His name shall be Je - sus, Wonderful name, wonderful name; His

1st time.   *rit.*

name shall be Je-sus, for He shall save His peo-ple from their sins.

2nd time.

name shall be Je - sus for He shall save His peo - ple from their sins.

66 Wonderful, Wonderful Jesus is to Me

H.L.

HALDOR LILLENAS.

Won-der-ful, won-der-ful, Je-sus is to me, Counsel-lor,

Prince of Peace; Mighty God is He; Sav-ing me, keeping me,

From all sin and shame, Wonderful is my Redeemer, praise His name!

67 I have been Alone with Jesus

Words used by permission.

MRS. R. R. FORMAN.

I've been a-lone with Je - sus, My bless-ed bless-ed Je-sus,

I've been a-lone with Je - sus, In the sunshine of His smile.

Yes, He will

T. M. Eastwood.

C. Austin Miles.

Yes, he will, Yes, he will, Yes, he will, Yes, he will, All his pro-mi-ses are

true, He will keep his word to you; Yes, he will, Yes, he will, yes, he

will, (yes, he will,) He will keep his word with you.

Friendship with Jesus

J.C.L.

Rev. J. C. Ludgate.

Friend - ship with Je - sus, Fel - low-ship Di - vine;

Oh, what blessed sweet commun - ion, Je - sus is a Friend of mine.

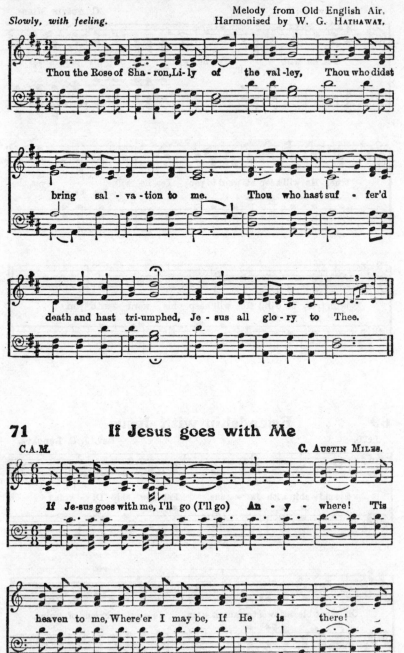

70 **The Rose of Sharon**

Slowly, with feeling.

Melody from Old English Air.
Harmonised by W. G. HATHAWAY.

Thou the Rose of Sha - ron, Li - ly of the val - ley, Thou who didst

bring sal - va - tion to me. Thou who hast suf - fer'd

death and hast tri - umphed, Je - sus all glo - ry to Thee.

71 **If Jesus goes with Me**

C.A.M.

C. AUSTIN MILES.

If Je - sus goes with me, I'll go (I'll go) An - y - where! 'Tis

heaven to me, Where'er I may be, If He is there!

count it a pri-vi-lege here His cross to bear; If
His cross, His cross, His cross to bear;

Je-sus goes with me I'll go An-y--where!

72   He's Coming for Me, One Day

W.G.H.   W. G. HATHAWAY.

Brightly.

He brought me out of the mi-ry clay and set my feet on a Rock; He

taught me how to watch and pray and made me one of His flock; He's a

Shepherd who leads me by His hand throughout my pil-grim way, And

rit.

now I'm look-ing for His re-turn, For He's coming for me one day.

We Worship and Adore Thee

Slowly.

Arr. by W. G. HATHAWAY.

We wor - ship and a - dore Thee, Fall - ing down be - fore Thee,

Songs of prais - es singing; ... Hal - le - lu - jahs ringing, Hal - le -

lu - jah! Hal-le - lu - jah! Hal-le - lu - jah!   A - men.

74

The End is not Yet

E. D. ELLIOT.

WM. EDIE MARKS.

And the end is not yet, praise the Lord; And the end is not yet,
praise the Lord;

praise the Lord; Bless-ings new He's still be - stowing, And my
praise the Lord;

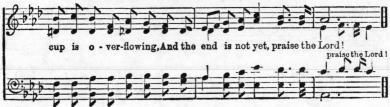

cup is o-ver-flowing, And the end is not yet, praise the Lord!

praise the Lord!

75   ## I Believe It : Do You?

Inscribed to Pastor E. J. Phillips.

SETH SYKES.

MR. & MRS. S. SYKES.

The Gos-pel is the pow'r of God un-to sal-va-tion, I be-

lieve it— yes, I be-lieve it! And who-so-ev-er will be-lieve will

find a full sal-va-tion, Hal-le-lu-jah to the Lamb! Praise the

Lord, I know 'tis true, If you test it, so will you. The

Gospel is the pow'r of God un-to sal-va-tion, I be-lieve it— do you?

76 Beauty for Ashes

J.G.C.

J. G. Crabbe.

He gives me joy............ in place of sor - - - row;
He gives me joy in place of care;

He gives me love.......... that casts out fear; He
He gives me love that casts out fear;

gives me sunshine for my sha - dow, And "beauty for ash-es," here.

77 Oh! it is Wonderful

M. J. Rosemoon.

Grant C. Tullar.

Oh, it is won-der-ful, so ve - ry won-der-ful, That we by

rit. *a tempo.*

grace should be Saved thro' e - ter - ni - ty; Oh, it is won-der-ful,

So ve-ry won-der-ful, That He should suf-fer on Cal-v'ry for me.

78   Travel by the Sunshine Line

S. SYKES.   MR. & MRS. SETH SYKES.

When you tra-vel by the Sunshine Line, When you tra-vel by the Sun-shine

Line,   There is joy and gladness, And no room for sadness, For 'tis

sum-mer all the time. When you tra-vel by the Sunshine Line,   The

heav'nly mu-sic is sub-lime, Know your sins for-gi-ven, Book right

through to hea-ven, Mind you tra-vel on the Sun-shine Line.

D.I.   DANIEL IVERSON.

Spi - rit of the liv - ing God, fall fresh on me; Spi - rit of the

liv-ing God, fall fresh on me. Break me! Melt me! Mould me!

Fill me! Spi - rit of the liv - ing God, fall fresh on me.

This chorus was written and composed in February, 1926, by Rev. Daniel Iverson.

80   **We Praise Thee, Bless Thee**

Slowly, and with expression.   Arr. by W. G. HATHAWAY.

We praise Thee, bless Thee, wor-ship and a - dore;

Fa - ther, Son, and Spi - rit for ev - er - more.

81   Once More Lord!

Arr. by Mr. & Mrs. Seth Sykes.

Once more, Lord, once more, Lord, As in the days of yore, On

this dear land Thy Spi - rit pour, Set Scotland now on fire!

The name of any other country may be substituted for Scotland.

82   It is Glory just to Walk with Him

M. Burgeson.   H. Lillenas.

It is glo - ry just to walk with Him, ... It is glo - ry just to
walk with Him,

walk with Him, ... He will guide my steps a - right, Thro' the
walk with Him,

vale and o'er the height; It is glo - ry just to walk with Him ......
walk with Him.

83 He is Mine, this Wonderful Saviour

Slowly, with expression.

Arr. by W. G. Hathaway.

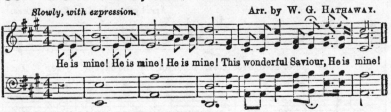

He is mine! He is mine! He is mine! This wonderful Saviour, He is mine!

84 God is Still on the Throne

Mrs. F.W.S.

Mrs. F. W. Suffield.

God is still on the throne, ... and He will re-mem-ber His
God ..... is still on the throne,

own; ... Tho' tri-als may press us and bur-dens dis-tress us, He

ne-ver will leave us a-lone; .. God is still on the
God .... is

throne, ... And He will re-mem-ber His own; His
still on the throne,

prom-ise is true, He will not forget you, God is still on the throne.

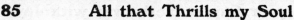

85   All that Thrills my Soul

T.H.

THORO HARRIS.

All that thrills my soul is Je - sus, He is more than life to me, (to me ;)

And the fairest of ten thou - sand, In my blessed Lord I see.

86   He Died for Me

A.W.E.   **Air** from "Call of the Angelus," adapted by A. W. EDSOR.

Slowly, with expression.

On Cal-v'ry's tree He died for me, That I His

love might know...... To set me free

He died for me, Oh, how I love Him so.

Published by permission of J. R. Lafleur and Son, Ltd., 8—10, Denman Street, Piccadilly Circus, London, W.1. England, who will be pleased to supply "Call of the Angelus" for Piano, Violin and Piano, Orchestra, or Military Band. Prices on application.

87 When your Cup runneth over with Joy

Arr. by W. G. HATHAWAY.

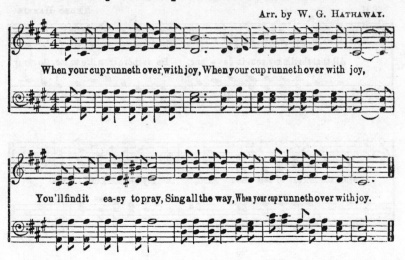

When your cup runneth over with joy, When your cup runneth over with joy,

You'll find it ea-sy to pray, Sing all the way, When your cup runneth over with joy.

88 Dearer than All

A.H.A.

ALFRED H. ACKLEY.

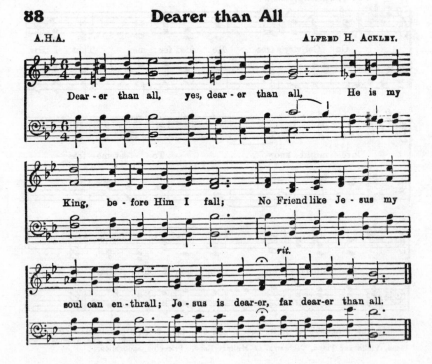

Dear-er than all, yes, dear-er than all, He is my

King, be-fore Him I fall; No Friend like Je-sus my

soul can en-thrall; Je-sus is dear-er, far dear-er than all.

89 Wonderful Jesus!

Annie. B. Russell.

Ernest O. Sellers.

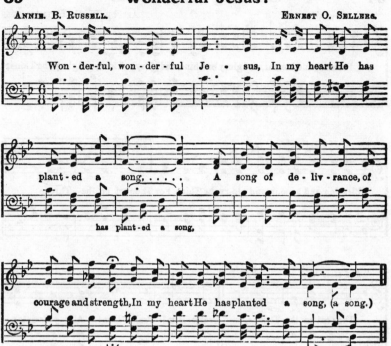

Won-der-ful, won-der-ful Je - sus, In my heart He has plant-ed a song,..... A song of de-liv-rance, of courage and strength, In my heart He has planted a song, (a song.)

has plant-ed a song,

90 Jesus has Lifted Me

Avis Burgeson.

Haldor Lillenas.

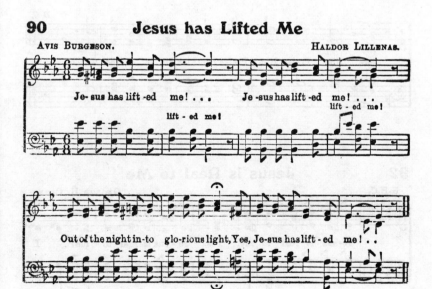

Je- sus has lift -ed me!... Je -sus has lift -ed me!...

lift - ed me!

lift - ed me!

Out of the night in-to glo-rious light, Yes, Je-sus has lift-ed me!..

Blessing and Honour

Arr. by W. G. HATHAWAY.

Blessing, and honour, and glory be Thine, and glory be Thine, and glory be Thine;

Blessing, and honour, and glo-ry be Thine, For Thou art on the Throne;

Thou art on the Throne. Praise Him! Praise Him! All ye saints a-

dore Him. Praise Him! Praise Him! for He is on the Throne.

92

Jesus is Real to Me

G. H. C.

GEORGE H. CARR.

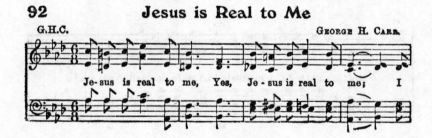

Je-sus is real to me, Yes, Je-sus is real to me; I

Jesus is Real to Me (Continued)

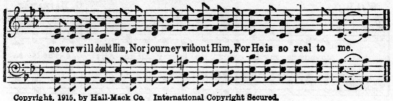

never will doubt Him, Nor journey without Him, For He is so real to me.

93 No Disappointment in Heaven

F. M. LEHMAN.   F.M.L.—CLAUDIA LEHMAN.

I'm bound for that beauti-ful ci-ty My Lord has prepar'd for His own, Where all the re-deem'd of all a-ges Sing 'Glo-ry' a-round the white throne; Some-times I grow home sick for Hea-ven, And the glo-ries I there shall be-hold; What a joy it will be when my Sa-viour I see, In that beauti-ful ci-ty of gold!

94 His Name is Precious

W.G.H.

W. G. HATHAWAY.

Je-sus is my Sa - viour, He is my All in All; Jesus is so dear to me, (so dear to me), I've an-swer'd at His call, And yielded Him my all, And His Name is precious to me.

95 Praise the Lord, what a joy is mine!

W.H.B.

W. H. BROWN.

Praise the Lord, what a joy is mine! Hal-le-lu-jah, I've a peace di-vine! Round my heart doth His love en-twine, Singing on the way; Halle - lu - jan!

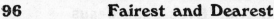

96 Fairest and Dearest

G.T.F.

MR. & MRS. SETH SYKES.

Fair - est and dear - rest, rar - est of all; ... Je - sus the

Flow - er of .... heaven, .. Sweet - est and pur - est ..

far - a - bove all, .. Je - sus my own Rose of Sha - ron. ..

97 Heaven's Jubilee is Near

We're marching heav'nward, This is our watch-word; Je-sus will soon be here.

This keeps us singing, Joybells are ringing, Heaven's ju-bi-lee is near.

98 **Turn your Eyes upon Jesus**

H.H.L. HELEN HOWARTH LEMMEL.

With expression.

Turn your eyes up-on Je - - sus, Look full in His

won - der -ful face;...... And the things of earth will grow

strange-ly dim In the light of His glo - ry and grace....

_Used by permission.

99 **Oh, What Love**

A. E. A. H. A. E. A. HAYWARD.

Slowly, with expression.

God, in His re-deem - ing love, Sent His

Son from heaven a - bove, Dy - ing on Cal - va - ry,

Shed-ding His blood for me; Oh! what Love.....

100 Rejoice, O Happy Soul!

T.B.B.

UNISON.

T. B. BARRETT.

Sing forth, O hap-py soul, God is thine all in all! Thy

wond'ring eyes will soon See heaven's sunlit coast; Redeem'd, and ever free From

HARMONY.

Sa-tan's ty-ran-ny, A - wait with joy the heav'n-ly host! . .

101 I'm Going On

R. E. DARRAGH.

A. W. EDSOR.

I'm go-ing on what ev - er be the cost; I'm go-ing

on, counting all but loss; I'm go - ing on,

He will lead the way, Going on with Jesus to that per-fect day.

He'll Take You Through

arr.

He'll take you through, ... How-ever you're tried; ......
He'll take you through, Howev-er you're tried;

His ten-der care .... is never de-nied. ....
His ten-der care is ne'er de-nied.

Be-lieve His Word, ... His promise is true. ....
Be-lieve His Word, His promise is true.

rit.

He'll take you through, ... He'll take you through. ......
He'll take you thro' He'll take you thro'.

103 Constantly Abiding

MRS. W.L.M. MRS. WILL L. MURPHY.

Con- -stant-ly a-bid- -ing, Je- -sus is
Con-stant-ly a-bid-ing, con-stant-ly a-bid-ing, Je-sus is mine, yes,

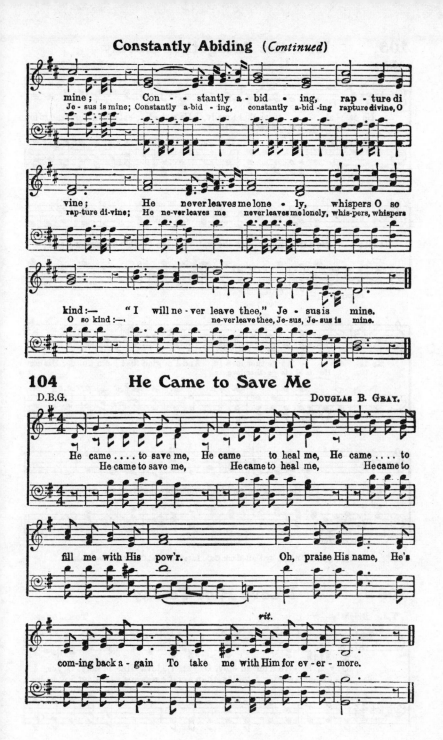

mine; Con - - stantly a - bid - ing, rap - ture di
Je - sus is mine; Constantly a - bid - ing, constantly a - bid - ing rapture divine, O

vine; He never leaves me lone - ly, whispers O so
rap-ture di-vine; He ne-ver leaves me never leaves me lonely, whis-pers, whispers

kind:— "I will ne - ver leave thee," Je - sus is mine.
O so kind :—I ne-ver leave thee, Je-sus, Je-sus is mine.

104 He Came to Save Me

D.B.G.   DOUGLAS B. GRAY.

He came .... to save me, He came to heal me, He came .... to
He came to save me, He came to heal me, He came to

fill me with His pow'r.   Oh, praise His name, He's

rit.

com-ing back a - gain To take me with Him for ev - er - more.

He's the Altogether Lovely

C.A.M.

C. AUSTIN MILES.

He is al - - to-ge-ther love-ly, He's the fair-est of ten thousand to my

He is al - to-ge-ther love-ly,

soul; He's the lil-y of the val-ley, the bright and morning star;

to my soul;

He is al - - to-ge-ther love-ly, And I'm glad that I am un-der His con-

He is al-to-ge-ther love-ly,

trol; For He feeds me and leads me where the green pas-tures are.

His control;

106   I Love Him To-day

T.J. *Brightly.*

TOM JONES.

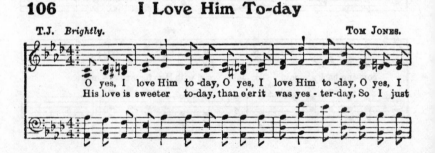

O yes, I love Him to -day, O yes, I love Him to -day, O yes, I

His love is sweeter to-day, than e'er it was yes - ter-day, So I just

I Love Him To-day (*Continued*)

love Him thro' all the day .. love Him thro' all the day ...

107   Saved! Saved! Saved!

Words and Music by SETH SYKES.   Harmonised by MR. & MRS. S. SYKES.

I'm saved, saved, saved, I'm trusting in Je-sus the Lord,

Saved, saved, saved, thro' faith in the Liv - ing Word. I'm

saved, saved, saved, I now am a child of God;

Je -sus is my lov-ing Sa - viour, and I'm saved, saved, saved.

FRANK HORNER.   MR. & MRS. SETH SYKES.

Je-sus my Sa-viour, Je-sus my Sa-viour, Dear-est of

all friends He is to me;..... When I am lone-ly,

I trust Him on-ly, Con-stant com-pan-ion I've prov'd Him to be..

109   **Jesus, Thou Loving Saviour**

Harmonised by W. G. HATHAWAY.

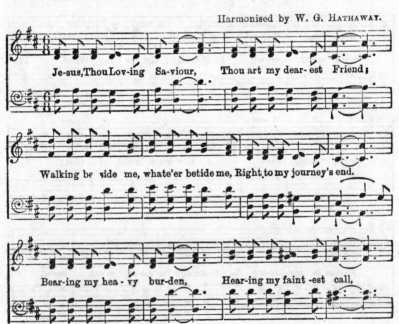

Je-sus, Thou Lov-ing Sa-viour, Thou art my dear-est Friend;

Walking be side me, whate'er betide me, Right to my journey's end.

Bear-ing my hea-vy bur-den, Hear-ing my faint-est call,

Thou art in earth and hea-ven, Je-sus, best of all . . .

110   He's Coming Soon, O Happy Day

W.G.H.

W. G. HATHAWAY.

(2nd Part.) Je-sus is the Rock of my Sal - vation and I know,

(1st Part.) Jesus blessed Je - sus,   Jesus blessed Je-sus, Je-sus is the name that thrills my

soul;   Whis-per it so soft-ly in the twi - light,

Sing it as you jour-ney on your way,   Shout it in the joy of your sal-

va - tion, For He's com-ing soon, O hap-py, hap-py day.

Note.—The Alto (1st Part) is the Air and should be sung by the Congregation. The Soprano (2nd Part) should only be sung by a few selected voices.

111 The Spirit Answers to the Blood

C. WESLEY.　　　　　　　　　　　　　　　　J. GOSTICK.

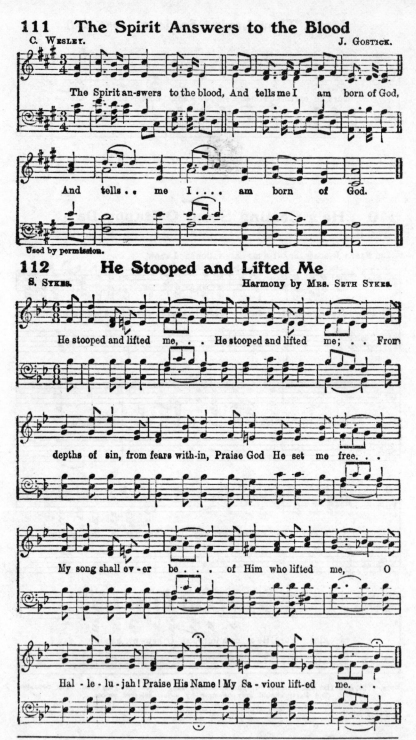

The Spirit an-swers to the blood, And tells me I am born of God,

And tells .. me I .... am born of God.

Used by permission.

112 He Stooped and Lifted Me

S. SYKES.　　　　　　　　　Harmony by MRS. SETH SYKES.

He stooped and lifted me, . . He stooped and lifted me; . . From

depths of sin, from fears with-in, Praise God He set me free. . .

My song shall ev - er be . . . of Him who lifted me, O

Hal - le - lu - jah! Praise His Name! My Sa - viour lift-ed me. . .

Elim Publishing Co., Ltd., Clapham Crescent, S.W.4—

Elim Choruses, No. 3

113   ## I Am the Door

Adapted

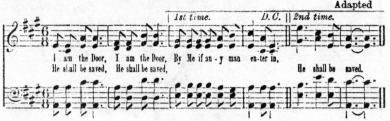

I am the Door, I am the Door, By Me if an-y man en-ter in,
He shall be saved, He shall be saved,

He shall be saved.

114   ## Sailing Home!

ELSIE DUNCAN YALE.   C. AUSTIN MILES.

Sail - ing   home, . . .   sail - ing   home! . . .
Sail - ing, sail-ing, sail - ing home,   sail - ing, sail - ing, sail - ing home!

O - ver the o - cean, deep and wide, And o'er   the   storm - y tide; We're
And o'er, and o'er the storm - y tide; We're

sail - ing   home, . . .   sail - ing   home! . . . And
sail - ing, sail-ing,   ail-ing home! We're sail-ing, sail - ing, sail-ing home! And

Je - sus shall our Pi - lot be; We're sail - ing   home! . .
sailing home.

115 Since Jesus came into my Heart

R. H. MAC. DANIEL.

CHAS. H. GABRIEL.

Since Je-sus came in-to my heart, Since Je-sus came
Since Je-sus came in, came in-to my heart, Since Je-sus came

in-to my heart, Floods of joy o'er my soul like the
in, came in-to my heart.

sea - bil - lows roll, Since Je-sus came in-to my heart.

116 The Wonderful One

Arranged by Mr. and Mrs. SETH SYKES.

1. They say He is won-der-ful, They say He is won-der-ful; The
2. I know He is won-der-ful, I know He is won-der-ful; He

sun and the moon and the stars a- bove All say He is won-der-ful.
saves and He keeps and He sat - is - fies—I know He is won-der-ful.

117 Pentecostal Fire is Falling

G.B. *Martial style.* GEORGE BENNARD.

Pen-te-cost-al fire is fall-ing, Praise the Lord, it fell on me,

Pen-te-cost-al fire is fall-ing, Brother, Sis-ter, let it fall on you!

118 Hallelujah, Amen

M. GENSICHEN.

Hal - le - lu -jah, Hal - le - lu -jah, Hal - le - lu - jah, A - men.

Hal - le - lu - jah, Hal - le - lu - jah, Hal - le - lu - jah, A - men.

Hal - le - lu -jah, Hal - le - lu - jah, Hal - le - lu - jah, A - men.

Hal - le - lu - jah, Hal - le - lu - jah, Hal - le - lu - jah, A - men.

119 **One Day**

Rev. J. Wilbur Chapman, D.D.　　　　　Chas. H. Marsh.

Liv-ing, He loved me; dy-ing, He saved me; Bur-ied, He

car-ried my sins far a-way, Ris-ing, He jus-ti-fied,

freely or ev-er: One day He's com-ing—O glo-ri-ous day.

120 **Give me a Heart like Thine**

J. H. Cole, (arr.)

1. Give me a heart like Thine, Give me a heart like Thine,
2. Give me a love like Thine, Give me a love like Thine,
3. Give me a faith like Thine, Give me a faith like Thine, } By Thy wonderful
4. Give me a joy like Thine, Give me a joy like Thine,
5. Give me a will like Thine, Give me a will like Thine,

pow-er, By Thy grace ev-'ry hour, Give {
me a heart like Thine.
me a love like Thine.
me a faith like Thine.
me a joy like Thine.
me a will like Thine.
}

121   **I'm going Through, Jesus**

H.B.

HERBERT BUFFUM.

I'm go-ing thro' yes, I'm go-ing thro'; I'll pay the
price, what-ev-er o-thers do; I'll take the way with the
Lord's des-pis-ed few, I'm go-ing thro', Je-sus, I'm going thro'

122   **If God be for us**

If God be for us who can be against? If God be for us
who can be against? If God be for us who can be a-gainst? He
that is with us might-ier is Than all that be a-gainst.

123 I've pitched my Tent in Beulah

C.A.M.

C. Austin Miles.

I've pitch'd my tent in Beulah With Je-sus to stay, My nights are full with music, With
I'v pitch'd my tent With Je-sus to stay, In peace by night, And

1st time only.

com-fort the day; And there is peace that passeth knowledge And blessing al-way, Since
com-fort by day;

2nd time only.

I have pitch'd my tent in Beu - lah. peace that passeth knowledge And

bless-ing al - way Since I have pitch'd my tent in Beu - lah.

124 Sweeter than All

Rev. J. Oatman, Jnr.

J. Howard Entwisle.

Je-sus is now and ev-er will be Sweeter than all the world to me,

Since I heard His lov-ing call,—Sweeter than all, Sweeter than all.

125   We will talk it o'er together

Mrs. C. H. M.

Mrs. C. H. Morris.

We will talk it o'er to-gether by and by, ... When we reach that ho-ly
by and by,
ci-ty you and I, ... How thro' faith we've o-ver-come, and have
reach'd our heav'nly home; We will talk it o'er to-ge-ther by and by.

126   'Tis Burning in my Soul

Delia T. White.

Wm. J. Kirkpatrick.

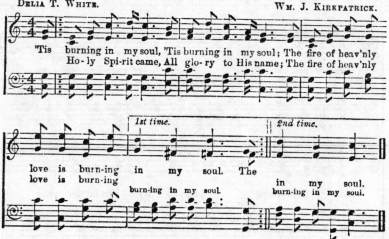

'Tis burning in my soul, 'Tis burning in my soul; The fire of heav'nly
Ho-ly Spi-rit came, All glo-ry to His name; The fire of heav'nly

1st time.
2nd time.

love is burn-ing in my soul. The
love is burn-ing   in my soul.
burn-ing in my soul.
burn-ing in my soul.

Hiding in Thee

W. O. CUSHING.

IRA D. SANKEY.

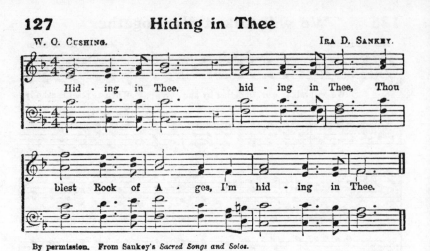

Hid - ing in Thee. hid - ing in Thee, Thou

blest Rock of A - ges, I'm hid - ing in Thee.

Caught up to meet Him

T.H.

THORO HARRIS, (arr.)

We'll be caught up to meet Him in the air, We'll be caught up His
to meet Him in the air;

bless-ed - ness to share; Ve - ry soon He will come To
His blessedness to share;

take His peo-ple home Caught up to meet Him in the air.
(and we'll be)

129 **Wonderful Treasure**

H. PALMER.

What a won-der-ful trea - sure, Gift of God without mea - sure;

We will tra-vel to-ge - ther, My Bi-ble and I. . . . .

130 **I will Guide Thee**

N. NILES.

P. P. BLISS.

"I will guide thee, I will guide thee, I will guide thee with Mine eye;

On the way from earth to hea - ven, I will guide thee with mine eye.

131 **His Yoke is Easy**

R. E. HUDSON.

His yoke is ea-sy, His bur-den is light, I've found it so, I've found it so;

He lead-eth me by day and by night, Where liv-ing wa-ters flow.

132 Holiness unto the Lord

C. H. M.

Mrs. C. H. Morris.

"Ho-li-ness unto the Lord," is our watchword and song, "Ho-li-ness un-to the

Lord," as we're marching a-long; Sing it, shout it,
"Ho-li-ness un-to the Lord," Sing

loud and long, "Ho-li-ness unto the Lord," now and forev-er.
"Ho-li-ness un-to the Lord,"

133 Can you Wonder?

Can you wonder? Can you wonder? Can you won-der why it is I love Him

so? (Can you won der) When I think of all He's done, and for

me the guil-ty one, Can you won-der why it is I love Him so?

Follow on!

REV. W. O. CUSHING.   REV R. LOWRY.

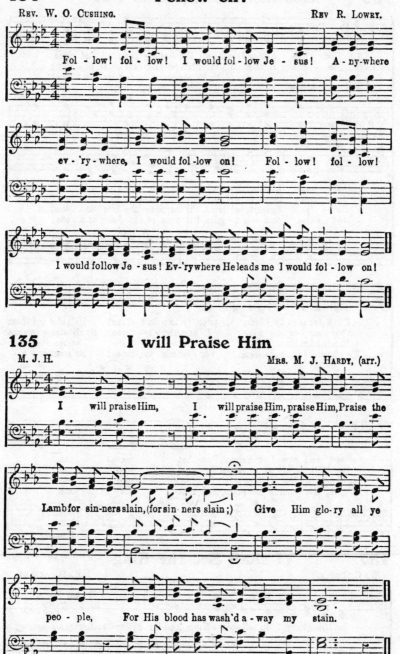

Fol - low! fol - low! I would fol - low Je - sus! A - ny-where ev - 'ry - where, I would fol -low on! Fol - low ! fol - low! I would follow Je - sus! Ev-'rywhere He leads me I would fol - low on!

I will Praise Him

M. J. H.   MRS. M. J. HARDY, (arr.)

I will praise Him, I will praise Him, praise Him, Praise the Lamb for sin-ners slain, (for sin - ners slain;) Give Him glo-ry all ye peo - ple, For His blood has wash'd a - way my stain.

1. God has blot-ted them out, I'm hap-py and glad and free;
2. Je - sus Heal-er di - vine, His pow'r is the same to - day;
3. Ho - ly Spi - rit of truth, our ser-vice de-pends on Thee;
4. Je - sus is com-ing a - gain, he's com-ing a - gain for me;

God has blot-ted them out, I'll turn to I-saiah and see;
Je - sus Heal-er di - vine, then what does the Bi - ble say?
Ho - ly Spi - rit of truth, I'll turn to the Acts and see;
Je - sus is com-ing a - gain, I'll turn to St. John and see;

Chap-ter for - ty -four, twen ty-two and three; He's blot-ted them
Ver - ses four and five, I - saiah fif - ty-three; By His stripes we are
Read and mark and learn, chap-ter one to three; The need of the
The chapter is four - teen, ver - ses one to three; He's coming a -

out, and now I can shout, For that means me.
heal'd, this truth is re-veal'd To you and me.
hour, is Ho - ly Ghost pow'r On you and me.
gain, His word is so plain, And that for me.

137 **I shall See the King**

W. C. POOLE.   B. D. ACKLEY.

In His glo-ry, I shall see the King, And for ev - er endless prais-es sing;

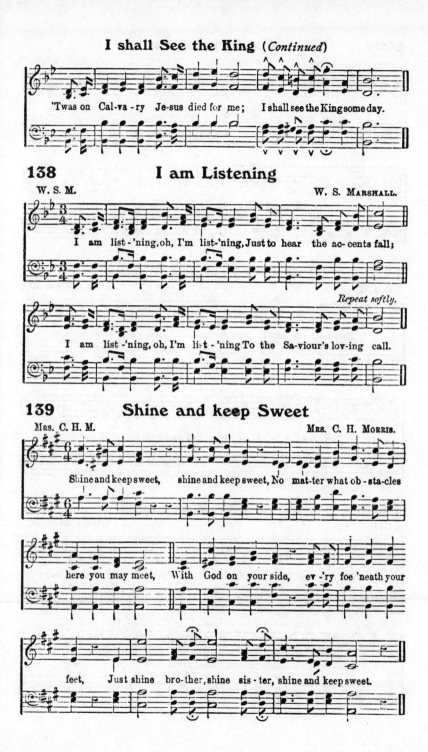

'Twas on Cal-va-ry Je-sus died for me; I shall see the King some day.

138   I am Listening

W. S. M.

W. S. MARSHALL.

I am list-'ning, oh, I'm list-'ning, Just to hear the ac-cents fall;

Repeat softly.

I am list-'ning, oh, I'm list-'ning To the Sa-viour's lov-ing call.

139   Shine and keep Sweet

MRS. C. H. M.

MRS. C. H. MORRIS.

Shine and keep sweet, shine and keep sweet, No mat-ter what ob-sta-cles

here you may meet, With God on your side, ev-'ry foe 'neath your

feet, Just shine bro-ther, shine sis-ter, shine and keep sweet.

140

Wonderful Jesus

Rev. W. J. Stuart.

Jno. R. Sweney.

Wonderful, wonderful Jesus! Won-der-ful, won-der-ful Je - sus!

Oh! He's a won-der-ful Sa - viour, Bless His ho - ly Name!

141

The Finest of the Wheat

F. A. G.

F. A. Graves.

Bread of life it is now to me, Hon - ey, wine and meat;

In Thy love I will ev - er be Fed up-on the fin-est of the wheat.

142

Have Thy Way, Lord

G. B.

George Bennard.

Have Thy way, Lord, have Thy way, This with all my heart I say;

I'll o-bey Thee come what may, Dear Lord, have Thy way.

143   Bring your Vessels, not a Few

Mrs. C. H. M.

Mrs. C. H. Morris.

He will fill your heart to-day to o-ver-flow - - - ing, As the
He will fill your heart to o-ver-flow-ing,

Lord commandeth you, 'Bring your vessels, not a few;' He will fill your heart to
He will fill

day to o-ver-flow - - ing With the Ho-ly Ghost and pow'r.
your heart to o-ver-flow-ing

144   Rich are the Moments

Fanny J. Crosby.

Jno. R. Sweney.

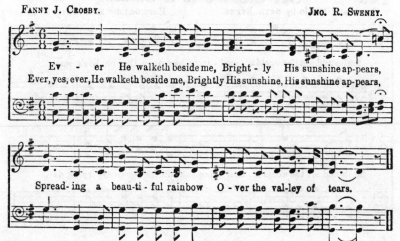

Ev - er He walketh beside me, Bright-ly His sunshine ap-pears,
Ever, yes, ever, He walketh beside me, Brightly His sunshine, His sunshine ap-pears,

Spread-ing a beau-ti-ful rainbow O-ver the val-ley of tears.

145 Leave it There

C. ALBERT TINDLEY.
Moderato.

Arr. by CHAS. A. TINDLEY, Jr.

Leave it there, ... leave it there, ... Take your bur-den to the
leave it there,   leave it there,

Lord and leave it there; .... If you trust and ne-ver doubt, He will
leave it there;

rit.

sure-ly bring you out; Take your bur-den to the Lord and leave it there.

146 Set the World a Smiling

Words and Music by SETH SYKES.

Harmony by MRS. SETH SYKES.

Smile and set the world a smil - ing, Cheer an-o-ther on life's way;

Smile and set the world a smil - ing. Smile for Je-sus ev-'ry day.

147   **I Would be Like Jesus**

JAMES ROWE.   B. D. ACKLEY.

Be like Je-sus, this my song, In the home and in the throng;

Be like Je-sus, all day long! I would be like Je-sus.

148   **Victory Ahead**

W.G.   REV. WILLIAM GRUM.

Vic-to-ry a-head! Vic-to-ry a-head! Thro' the blood of

Je-sus, vic-to-ry a-head; Trust-ing in the Lord, I

hear the conq'ror's tread, By faith I see the vic-to-ry a-head.

149   **Free!**

Arr. by W. G. Hathaway.

I am free, free, free!   Christ has made me free!

Once I was blind, but now I can see, For I am free, free, free!

150   **Trust in the Lord and don't despair**

Arr. by W. G. Hathaway.

Trust in the Lord and don't de-spair,   He is a Friend so true,

No mat-ter what your trou-bles are,   Je - sus will see you through;

Sing when the day is bright, Sing thro' the darkest night; Ev-'ry

day, all the way, Let us sing! sing! sing!

151 You may Look for Me

A. A. Payn.

C. Austin Miles.

You may look for me, for I'll be there, I'll be there, I'll be there, I'll be there,
I'll be there! I'll be there! You may look for me, for I'll be
there! I'll be there! Glo-ry to His name! precious name!

152 Man of Calvary

W.G.H.

Old English Air, arr. W.G.H.

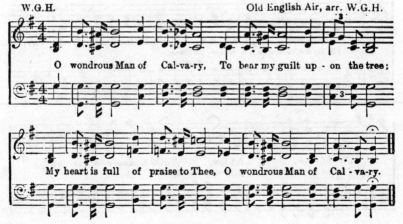

O wondrous Man of Cal-va-ry, To bear my guilt up-on the tree;
My heart is full of praise to Thee, O wondrous Man of Cal-va-ry.

153 In My Heart a Song is Ringing

In my heart a song is ring-ing; He has pardon'd me I

know, Just be-cause He loves me so, And I'm sing-ing, sing-ing,

rit.

sing-ing, Just be-cause He loves me so.

154 I'll Follow Jesus

W. J. H.
W. J. HENRY.

I'll fol-low, I'll fol-low, I'll fol-low Je-sus all the way;
I'll fol-low, fol-low on, I'll fol-low, fol-low on.

I'll fol-low, I'll fol-low, To the home of ev-er-last-ing day.
I'll fol-low, fol-low on, I'll fol-low, fol-low on,

My Jesus Saves

W. HARPER.

Londonderry Air, arr. by W. G. HATHAWAY.

My Je-sus saves, I know it for He saved me; My Je-sus heals, and

takes a-way all pain; My Je-sus fills me with the Ho-ly

Spi-rit, And one day He is com-ing back a-gain. Oh, yes, I

know I'm saved, oh Hal-le-lu-jah! And bap-tised too, O

glo-ry to His name! And now my all I give to Him in

ser-vice, The wondrous gos-pel of sal-va-tion to pro-claim.

156 Everybody Ought to Love Jesus

HARRY DIXON LOES.

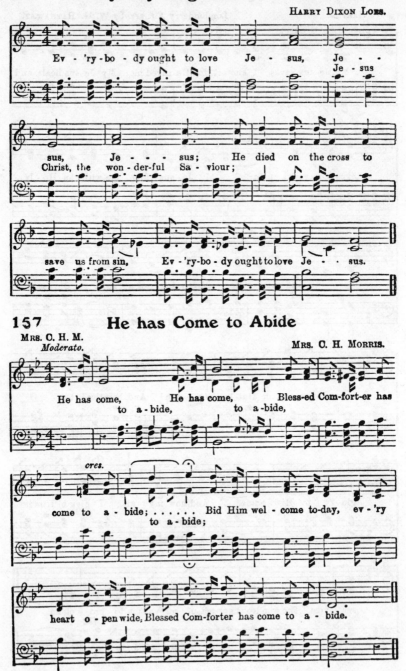

Ev - 'ry-bo - dy ought to love Je - sus, Je -
Je - sus

sus, Je - - - sus; He died on the cross to
Christ, the won - der-ful Sa - viour;

save us from sin, Ev - 'ry-bo - dy ought to love Je - - sus.

157 He has Come to Abide

MRS. C. H. M.
Moderato.

MRS. C. H. MORRIS.

He has come, He has come, Bless-ed Com-fort-er has
to a - bide, to a - bide,

cres.

come to a - bide; ...... Bid Him wel - come to-day, ev - 'ry
to a - bide;

heart o - pen wide, Blessed Com-forter has come to a - bide.

In the Sweet By and By

Arr. by W. G. HATHAWAY.

In the sweet by and by, In the sweet by and by ;

I have a mansion so bright and so fair, O what a joy when we all get there, In the

sweet by and by ; In the sweet by and by : When the

bat-tle is done and the vic-to-ry's won In the sweet by and by

159   The Old, Old Story

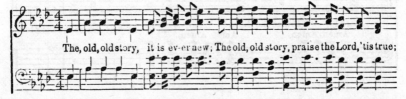

The, old, old story, it is ev-er new; The old, old story, praise the Lord, 'tis true;

That Je-sus died for me as well as you, Tell me the old, old sto - ry.

I am Glad I belong to Jesus

Arr. by W. G. HATHAWAY.

I am glad I be-long to Je - sus, I am glad I be-long to
I be - long to Je - sus, I be - long to

Je - sus, I am glad I be-long to Je - sus, Hal-le-
Je - sus. I be - long to Je - sus. Hal-le-

lu - jah, Praise the Lord, Praise the Lord! Praise the
A-men, A-men!

Lord! Praise the Lord! Praise the Lord! Praise the
Amen, Amen! Amen, Amen! Amen, A-men!

Lord! Praise the Lord!
Amen, Amen, Amen, Amen, Hal-le-lu-jah! Praise the Lord!

161 Steal Away to Jesus

Steal a-way, steal a-way, Steal a-way to Je - sus,

Steal away (Continued)

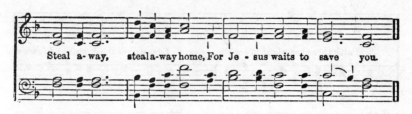

Steal a-way, steal a-way home, For Je-sus waits to save you.

162   Breathe upon Us

R. K. C. *Slow.*

R. KELSO CARTER.
rit.

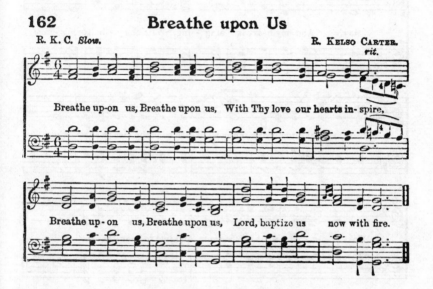

Breathe up-on us, Breathe upon us, With Thy love our hearts in-spire,

Breathe up-on us, Breathe upon us, Lord, baptize us now with fire.

163   Jesus Never Fails

A.A.L.

A. A. Luther.

Je-sus ne-ver fails! Je-sus ne-ver fails!

Heaven and earth may pass a-way, But Je-sus ne-ver fails!

Faith turns the night in-to the day, Love drives the doubts and fears a-
way, And my heart is sing - ing, With the joy-bells ring - ing;
List' to the pealing of its chimes, Faith wins the vict'ry ev'ry time—
Hal - le - lu - jah! what a Saviour, And just to know that He is mine.

165   I shall be like Him

W. A S.   REV. W. A. SPENCER, D.D.

I shall be like Him, I shall be like Him, And in His beauty shall shine,
I shall be like Him, wondrously like Him, Je-sus, my Sa-viour di - vine.

166   **Still it Flows**

Still it flows, still it flows, Still it flows as fresh as ev-er, Still it

flows as fresh as ev-er From my Saviour's wounded side.

167   **There's a Gladness in my Heart**

M.P.

M. POWNELL.
Harmony by MRS. SUTTON-REID.

There's a gladness in my heart to-day; Praise the Lord, Praise the Lord!

For my ma-ny sins are wash'd a-way; Hal-le - lu-jah, Praise the Lord!

I go sing-ing on my way, All my night has turn'd to day;

And e - ver by His side I'll stay; Hal-le - lu-jah, praise the Lord.

168 Calvary's Stream is Flowing

J. C. B.

J. C. BATEMAN.

Cal - va - ry's stream is flow-ing, . . . Cal - va - ry's

stream is flow - ing, . . . Flow-ing so free for

you and for me, Cal - va -ry's stream is flow- ing. . .

169 My Chains Fell Off

Arranged by DUNCAN McNEIL.

Largo.

My chains fell off; — My soul was free; — I rose; —

went forth, And fol - low'd Thee.

Presto.

My chains fell off, My

soul was free, — I rose, went forth, and fol - low'd Thee.

170 O I'm so Happy

Arr. by W. G. HATHAWAY.

O I'm so hap-py, so ve-ry hap-py, Since

Je-sus put the hap-py in my heart. No more I'm doubt-ing,

Instead, I'm shout-ing, Since Je-sus put the hap-py in my heart.

171 Keep Me True

N.E.M.

Prayerfully.

NELL E. MAYS.

Keep me true, Lord Je-sus, keep me true! . . . . . Keep me true, Lord
keep me true;

Je-sus, keep me true! There's a race that I must run, There are

vict'ries to be won, Give me pow'r, ev'ry hour, to be true!
true! to be true!

172 Changed in the Twinkling of an Eye

Arranged by W. G. HATHAWAY.

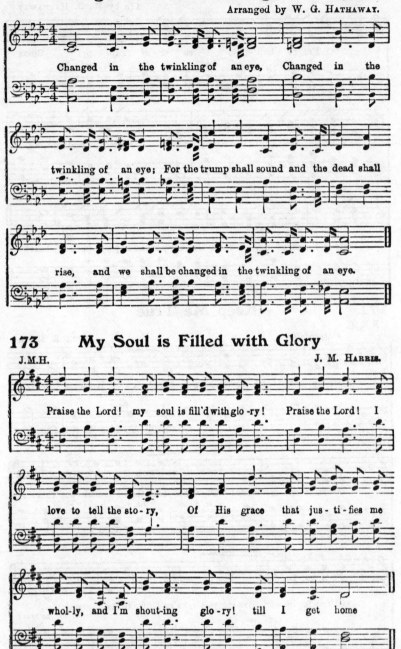

Changed in the twinkling of an eye, Changed in the twinkling of an eye; For the trump shall sound and the dead shall rise, and we shall be changed in the twinkling of an eye.

173 My Soul is Filled with Glory

J.M.H.

J. M. HARRIS.

Praise the Lord! my soul is fill'd with glo-ry! Praise the Lord! I love to tell the sto-ry, Of His grace that jus-ti-fies me whol-ly, and I'm shout-ing glo-ry! till I get home

174 **He is Coming**

E.A.H.   E. A. HINCHCLIFFE.

He is com-ing, Hal-le-lu-jah, We shall hear the midnight cry: Be-
hold the Bridegroom cometh, We shall meet Him, we shall greet Him bye and bye.

175 **Fishers of Men**

D. B. GRAY.   DOUGLAS B. GRAY.

Je-sus said "I will make you fish-ers of men;"
Je-sus said "I will make you fish-ers of men, Take
up thy cross and fol-low Me, and thou shalt My dis-ci-ples be!" Then
preach the Word, and fish-ers for Je-sus be.

176 It's Real

H.L.C.

H. L. Cox.

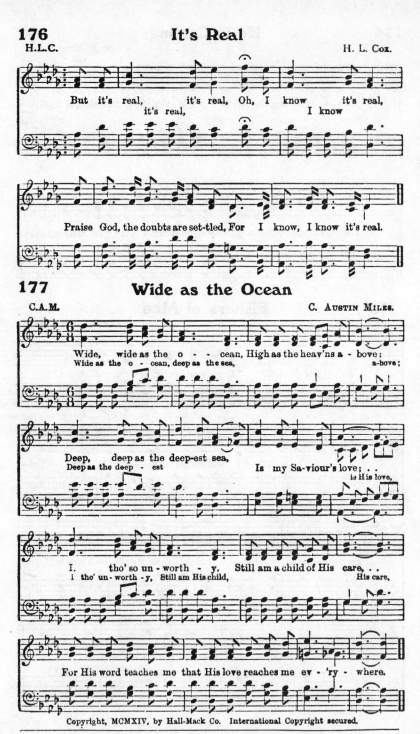

But it's real, it's real, Oh, I know it's real,
it's real, I know

Praise God, the doubts are set-tled, For I know, I know it's real.

177 Wide as the Ocean

C.A.M.

C. Austin Miles.

Wide, wide as the o - - cean, High as the heav'ns a - bove;
Wide as the o - cean, deep as the sea, a-bove;

Deep, deep as the deep-est sea, Is my Sa-viour's love; . .
Deep as the deep - est is His love,

I, tho' so un - worth - y, Still am a child of His care, . .
I tho' un - worth-y, Still am His child, His care,

For His word teaches me that His love reaches me ev - 'ry - where.

Elim Choruses No. 4

178   ## Moment by Moment

D. W. WHITTLE.

MAY WHITTLE MOODY.

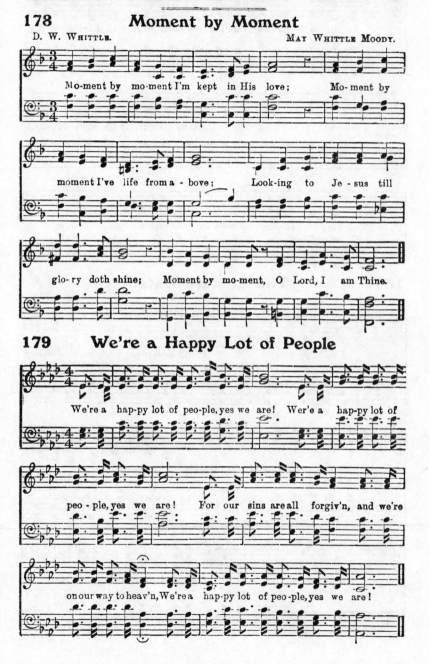

Moment by mo-ment I'm kept in His love; Mo-ment by

moment I've life from a - bove; Look-ing to Je - sus till

glo - ry doth shine; Moment by mo-ment, O Lord, I am Thine.

179   ## We're a Happy Lot of People

We're a hap-py lot of peo-ple, yes we are! Wer'e a hap-py lot of

peo - ple, yes we are! For our sins are all forgiv'n, and we're

on our way to heav'n, We're a hap-py lot of peo-ple, yes we are!

180 **In the Same Old Way**

H.B.

Arr. from HERBERT BUFFUM.

In the same old way, In the same old way, The Lord is do-ing
business in the same old way; In the same old way, In the same old way,
The Lord is do-ing business in the same old way.

181 **The Eastern Gate**

I.G.M.

Arr. by I.G.M.

I will meet you, in the morning, I will meet you, in the morning, Just in-
side the Eastern Gate o-ver there; I will meet you, in the morning,
I will meet you, in the morning, I will meet you in the morning o-ver there.

182   My All in All

EDGAR LEWIS.

L. E. JONES.

All in all, all in all, A strength in time of
Je-sus is my all in all, Je-sus is my all in all,

wea-ri-ness, a light where shadows fall, All in all,
Je-sus is my all in all,

all in all, Je-sus is my all in all.
Je-sus is my all in all,

183   The Bleeding Lamb

The Lamb, the Lamb, the bleed-ing Lamb, I

love the sound of Je-sus's name; It sets my spi-rit

all in a flame, Glo-ry to the bleed-ing Lamb.

184 Victory all the time

MRS. C.H.M.

MRS. C. H. MORRIS.

Vic-to-ry! vic-to-ry! precious blood-bought victory, Vic-to-ry!

Vic-to-ry! yes, vic-to-ry! yes,

Vic-to-ry! yes,

vic-to-ry! vic-t'ry all the time, As Je-ho-vah liv - eth,

vic-to-ry! yes,

Strength divine He giv - eth, Unto those who trust Him vict'ry all the time.

185 Our God is Just the Same

W.G.H.

W. G. HATHAWAY.

Marching time.

Our God is just the same, Now and al-ways, praise His name.

Yes-ter-day, to-day, for ev - er; From His love no pow'r can se - ver;

And His prom-ise fail - eth ne - ver, He's for aye the same.

aye, for aye the

186 Give me Oil in my Lamp

T.H.

THORO HARRIS.

Give me oil in my lamp, Oil in my lamp, Oil in my lamp, I pray; Give me oil in my lamp, Keep me shining in the camp Un-til the break of day.

187 I will Trust the Saviour

SIDNEY YOUNGSON.

JEAN E. H. YOUNGSON.

Moderately slow.

I will trust the Sa-viour now be-liev-ing, He died for me on Cal-va-ry, His gift of life, so great so free, Glad-ly I re-ceive.... Now I praise and fol-low Him re-joic-ing, For His grace is suf-fi-cient for me......

188   # The Pentecostal Power

Charlotte G. Homer.

Chas. H. Gabriel.

Lord, send the old-time pow'r, the Pen-te-cos-tal pow'r! Thy flood-gates of

blessing on us throw o-pen wide! Lord, send the old-time pow'r, the

Pen-te-cos-tal pow'r, That sinners be converted and Thy name glori - fied!

189   # Jesus has a Place for You

J. S. R.

J. S. R.

Come to - day and live for Je - sus, There's a lot of work to do;

God - li - ness pos-sessing, You can be a blessing, Je - sus has a

rall.

place for you,...... Yes! Je - sus has a place for you.

190 Alone with God

Rev. Johnson Oatman, Jr.   Wm. J. Kirkpatrick.

A-lone with God, ... the world for-bid-den, A-lone with
God, ... O blest re-treat; Alone with God, ... and in him
hid-den To hold with him . . . . . . com-mun-ion sweet.

191 Joy in My Soul

J.B.M.   J. B. MacKay.

There is joy in my soul, Oh, glo-ry Hal-le-lu-jah! Je-sus'
blood makes me whole! Oh, glo-ry Hal-le-lu-jah! His love and pow'r
di-vine has touch'd this heart of mine, And there's joy, yes, joy in my soul.

192 Bend me Lower

Slowly and prayerfully.　　　　　　　　　　　*rit.*

Bend me low-er, Bend me low-er, Bend me lower, Lower down at Je-su's feet.

193 Jesus is my Great Unchanging Friend

Words and Air by A. W. EDSOR.　　　Arrangement by A. E. A. HAYWARD.

Briskly.

Je - sus is my great un-chang-ing Friend,

Yes - ter - day, to - day, un-to the end;

He's the same for ev - ver, no change in Him I see,

rit. poco a poco . . . .

And I'll serve Him for His love to me. . . . .

194 The Blood shall Never Lose its Power

MRS. C. H. M.   MRS. C. H. MORRIS.

And the blood shall ne-ver lose its power,   No,
Je-sus' blood shall ne - - ver, ne-ver lose its power, No

ne - ver, ... no, ne - ver, ... Je-su's blood a-
ne-ver lose its power, no, ne-ver lose its power, Je-sus' blood a

rit.

vails for me for ev-er, ... It shall ne-ver lose its power.
me for ev-er,

195 I Love Jesus, Hallelujah!

Welsh air.

When I first commenc'd my journey, Peo-ple said I'd run a-way;
CHO.—I love Je-sus, hal-le-lu-jah! I love Je-sus, yes, I do.

But they all have been de-ceiv-èd, In the faith I'm still to-day.
I love Je-sus, He's my Sa-viour, Je-sus smiles and loves me too.

196   # Give God the Glory

Arr. by W. G. HATHAWAY.

Give God the glo-ry, He has done it all; Je-sus has re-deem'd me with His pre-cious blood. Give God the glo-ry, He has done it all. Je-sus has redeem'd me with His pre-cious blood.

197   # Calvary Love

Words and Air by M. K. CRAIG.   Harmony by B. TETCHNER.

Cal-va-ry love, Cal-va-ry love, Great heart of God re-veal it in me That sin-sick souls a-round may see Thy wonderful Cal-va-ry love. . . . . Cal-va-ry love.

198 Jesus, a Wonderful Saviour

W.G.H. *Worshipfully.*

W. G. HATHAWAY.

Je - sus, Je - sus, A wonderful Saviour is Je - sus,

Je - sus, Je - sus, A wonderful Saviour is Je - sus

199 Know your Bible

H.H.L.

H. H. LEMMEL.

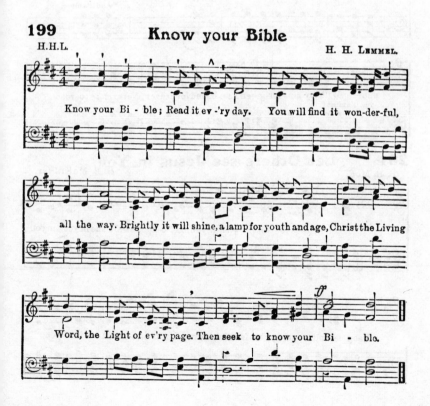

Know your Bi - ble; Read it ev -'ry day. You will find it won-der-ful,

all the way. Brightly it will shine, a lamp for youth and age, Christ the Living

Word, the Light of ev'ry page. Then seek to know your Bi - ble.

200 A New Name in Glory

C.A.M.

C. Austin Miles.

There's a new name written down in glory, And it's mine, oh, yes, it's mine!

And it's mine, yes, it's mine

And the white-robed angels sing the sto-ry, 'A sin-ner has come home;'

has come home;

For there's a new name written down in glo-ry, And it's mine, oh, yes, it's

And it's mine,

mine! With my sins for-given I am bound for heaven, Nevermore to roam.

yes, it's mine!

201 Let Others see Jesus in You

B. B. McK.

B. B. McKinney.

Let o-thers see Je-sus in you, (in you), Let o-thers see Je-sus in you, (in you),

Keep telling the sto-ry, be faithful, be true, Let o-thers see Je-sus in you.

202　The Need of the World is Jesus

A. W. EDSOR.
R. E. DARRAGH.
Harmonised by MISS B. TETCHNER.

The need of the world is Je - - sus, To sat - is -
fy its long - ing soul. The need of the world is
Je - - sus, To make it ev - 'ry whit whole...... The
need of the world is Je - - sus, to bear its
bur - dens and cares...... The need of the world is
Je - - sus, To an - swer it's ma - ny prayers.....

203 Out of the Mud and the Mire

THE 'TOLBOOTH' CHORUS.

Words and Music by MR. & MRS. SETH SYKES.

Out of the mud and the mire, .. Out of the mud and the mire,
I have been lift-ed by Christ to-day, Now I am sing-ing a-long my way—
Je-sus lift-ed me up, Out of the mud and the mire. . . .

204 If you have the Sunshine in your Heart

Words and Music by REV. TOM JONES.

If you have the sun-shine in your heart, If you have the
sunshine in your heart, Joy bells will be ring-ing, Hearts be tun'd to
sing-ing, If you have the sun-shine in your heart.

205 Smile, Brother, Smile

Words and Music by Rev. Tom Jones.

Smile, bro-ther, smile, God will not let you down,

Smile, bro-ther, smile, ... Take from your face that frown; ...

Things may be dark and drea - ry, Life hard to un - der - stand, ...

But God is waiting to help you, So smile, brother, smile. ...

206 I Know Someone Who Loves You

E.P.G.

Moderato.

E. P. Graham.

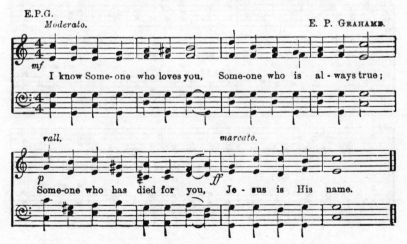

I know Some- one who loves you, Some-one who is al - ways true;

Some-one who has died for you, Je - sus is His name.

207 Victorious Life Chorus

B.A.B.

BENJ. A. BAUE.

With enthusiasm.

1. Have you been fill'd with the Ho-ly Ghost and pow-er, Is Je - sus
2. Yes, I've been fill'd with the Ho-ly Ghost and pow-er, Je-sus is

real to your heart and life this hour? Tar-ry be-fore Him un-
real to my heart and life this hour; Joy-bells are ring-ing, the

til the Lord of glo - ry Sends down from heaven the show'rs of lat-ter rain.
Ho - ly Ghost is sing-ing Prais-es to Je - sus, my Lord and coming King.

208 I Need Jesus

GEORGE O. WEBSTER.

CHAS. H. GABRIEL.

I need Je - sus, I need Je - sus, I need Je-sus ev-'ry
I need Je - sus with me, I need Je - sus al-ways,

day; . . . . Need Him in the sunshine hour, need Him when the
ev-'ry day;

I Need Jesus (*continued*)

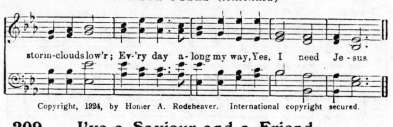

storm-clouds low'r; Ev-'ry day a-long my way, Yes, I need Je-sus.

209   I've a Saviour and a Friend

R. E. DARRAGH.   C. E. B. STUART.

I've a Sa-viour and a Friend Whose love is
true, ... Faith-ful al-ways to the end, ..
Plan-ning for you. Lift-ing bur-dens day by
day, Joy He gives a-long life's way, Sa-tis-
fies me, come what may, His name is Je-sus.

210 Tis Very Blessed to Meet with God

Translation by W. G. H.　　　　　　　　　H. R. PALMER, (adapted).

Meet-ing with Je-sus from day to day, Meet-ing the light of His
A chwrdd a'r Je-su o dydd i dydd, A chwrdd i fo-lu yn

cres.

faith on the way, .. Meet-ing the pow'r of His won-der-ful love, ..
go-leu y ffydd, A chwrdd a cha-riad ry-fe-dda sy'n bôd, A

ff

Meet-ing to praise Him in hea-ven a-bove, 'Tis ve-ry bless-ed to
chwrdd yn y ne-foedd i gan-u ei glôd, Mae'n fen-di ged-ig cael

dim.　　　　　　　*p*

meet with God, Meet with God, Meet with God, 'Tis ve-ry bless-ed to
chwrdd a Duw, Chwrdd a Duw, Chwrdd a Duw, Mae'n fen-di-ged-ig cael

p　　　　*pp rit.*

meet with God, Meet .. with God, Meet .. with God.
chwrdd a Duw, Chwrdd a Duw, Chwrdd a Duw.

211 When the Saints go Marching In

Arr. by W. G. HATHAWAY.

When the saints go marching in, When the saints go marching in;
When they crown Him Lord of all, When they crown Him Lord of all;

Lord, I want to be a-mong the number, When the saints go marching in.
Lord, I want to be a-mong the number, When they crown Him Lord of all.

212 My Wonderful Saviour Divine

QUEENIE ASHMORE.

MR. and MRS. SETH SYKES.

Je - sus, Sa-viour of mine, He is a Sa-viour di - vine,

When the way is dark and drear, He doth com-fort, help, and cheer;

He walks close by my side, In Him I can con-fide,

For I'm depending On His grace un-ending, This Sa - viour of mine.

213 The Lamb that was Slain

Arr. by W. G. Hathaway.

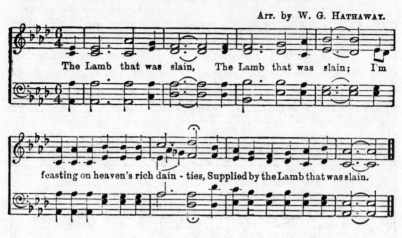

The Lamb that was slain, The Lamb that was slain; I'm feasting on heaven's rich dain - ties, Supplied by the Lamb that was slain.

214 The Power of God

F.A.G.

F. A. Graves.

The pow'r of God is just the same to- day, is just the same to-day, It does not matter what the peo - ple say; what the people say; What-ev - er God has promised He's a - ble to per-form, For the pow'r of God is just the same to - day.

215   Jesus, Thou Loving Saviour

G. PARKER.   Melody by H. PARKER.

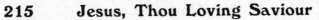

Je-sus, Thou loving Saviour, Je-sus, Thou blest Redeem-er, Shed-ding Thy blood for me, That I might pardon'd be. Je-sus, Thou great De-liv-'rer, Je-sus, Thou conqu'ring Saviour, Dy-ing on Cal-va-ry To set me free.

216   The Pentecostal Power is just the same

MRS. C.H.M.   MRS. C. H. MORRIS.

The pow'r, the pow'r, the Pen-te-cos-tal pow'r Is just the same to-day, Is just the same to-day; The pow'r, the pow'r, the wonder-working pow'r is just the same to-day.

217 He is the King of Love

REV. A. H. ACKLEY.

B. D. ACKLEY.

He is the King of Love, . . Changeless, transforming, di-vine, . . .
of Love, transforming, divine,

He is the King of my life, What a wonderful joy is mine! . .

Of His great love I'll sing, . . Sent from the Fa-ther a-bove,
I'll sing, the Fa-ther a-bove,

To Him for-ev-er my soul will cling, He is the King of Love. . . .
the King of Love.

218 I Remember Calvary

REV. W. C. MARTIN.

J. M. BLACK.

Jesus shall lead me night and day, Jesus shall lead me all the way;

I Remember Calvary (continued)

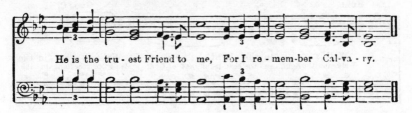

He is the tru-est Friend to me, For I re-mem-ber Cal-va-ry.

219 Let me Hide in Thee

MRS. J. I. McCLELLAND. J. LINCOLN HALL.

Let me hide in Thee, Re-fuge there for me,
my-self in Thee, in Thee, for me, for me, for me,

Where no e-vil shall be-fall me, And no fear can be.
no fear can be, can be.

Let me hide in Thee, Christ of Cal-va-ry,
my-self in Thee, Cal-va-ry, of Cal-va-ry,

Christ of res-ur-rec-tion ful-ness, Let me hide in Thee.
my-self, my-self in Thee.

Walk in the Light

ASA HULL.

GEO. C. HUGG.

Walk .... in the light! .... Walk .... in the
Walk in the light, in the beau-ti-ful light of God; Walk in the light, in the

light! .... Walk .... in the
beau-ti-ful light of God! Walk in the light, in the

light .... Walk in the light, the light of God!
beau-ti-ful light of God!

221

Till the Day Dawns

R.M.

ROBERT MATTHEWS.

Till the day dawns and the shadows flee a - way, flee a - way, Till the

day dawns and the shadows flee a - way, flee a-way; Guide me, O Thou dear Re-

deem-er, Keep me faith-ful all the way, Till the day dawns and the

Till the Day Dawns (*continued*)

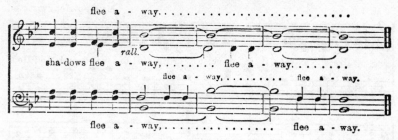

flee a - way.........................

sha-dows flee a - way,....... flee a-way.......

flee a - way,......... flee a - way.

flee a - way,........ flee a - way.

222

Trav'ling Home

Air by C. W. SLEMMING.
Harmony by W. H. MacILWAINE.

C. W. SLEMMING.

I'm trav'ling home to glo - ry, Trav'ling home, trav'ling home, The
I'm trav'ling home, I'm trav-'ling home,

daylight shines be - fore me, I'm trav-'ling, trav'ling home.

Trav - 'ling, trav-'ling home, I'm trav'ling home to glo - ry,

Trav - 'ling, trav-'ling home, I'm trav-'ling home to God.

223 I've a Saviour, O so Precious

M.H.

Muriel Honeysett.

I've a Sa-viour, O so precious. For He died to save my soul; And He'll
ne-ver, ne-ver leave me, While e-ter-nal a-ges roll; How ev-er
o-thers live without Him, Is a thing I can't ex-plain, For all I
need I find in Je-sus, Praise and bless His ho-ly name.

224 He's the Lamb on the Throne

Words and Melody by J. Kershaw.

Harmony by H. W. Fielding.

He's the Lamb on the throne, In-ter-ced - - ing for His
He's the Lamb on the throne, In-ter-ced-ing for His

own; With His blood shed for me, On Mount Cal-va-ry.
precious blood shed for me,

225 It isn't any trouble just to S-M-I-L-E

Arrangement by W. G. HATHAWAY.

It is-n't a-ny trou-ble just to S-M-I-L-E, It

is-n't a-ny trou-ble just to S-M-I-L-E.

Smile a-way your trouble, It will van-ish like a bub-ble if you

on-ly take the trou-ble just to S-M-I-L-E.

226 He Satisfies Me So!

H.D.L.

HARRY DIXON LOES.

rit.

He sat-is-fies me so, . . . His constant peace I know; . .
my long-ings so, with-in I know;

a tempo. — — *ad lib.*

My all I give for Him to live, He sat-is-fies me so!

Words and Melody by F. M. LEHMAN. Har. by MRS. C. LEHMAN MAYS.

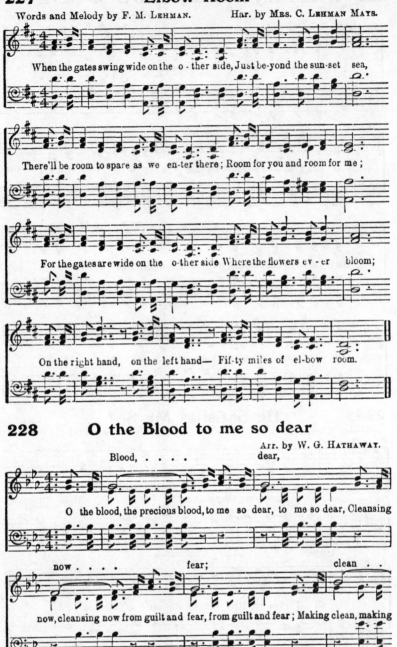

When the gates swing wide on the o - ther side, Just be-yond the sun-set sea,

There'll be room to spare as we en-ter there; Room for you and room for me;

For the gates are wide on the o-ther side Where the flowers ev - er bloom;

On the right hand, on the left hand— Fif-ty miles of el-bow room.

228 **O the Blood to me so dear**

Arr. by W. G. HATHAWAY.

Blood, ... dear,

O the blood, the precious blood, to me so dear, to me so dear, Cleansing

now . . . . fear; clean . .

now, cleansing now from guilt and fear, from guilt and fear; Making clean, making

O the Blood to me so dear *(continued)*

clean my heart with Thee, my heart with Thee, Cleansing now from self and sin.

229 By-and-By we'll See the King

Arr. by W. G. Hathaway.

By - and-by we'll see the King, By - and-by we'll see the King,

By - and-by we'll see the King and crown Him Lord of all, and

crown . . Him Lord of all, and crown . . Him Lord of all, and

crown . . Him Lord of all and crown Him Lord of all.

Clear are the Skies above Me

Arr. by W. G. HATHAWAY.

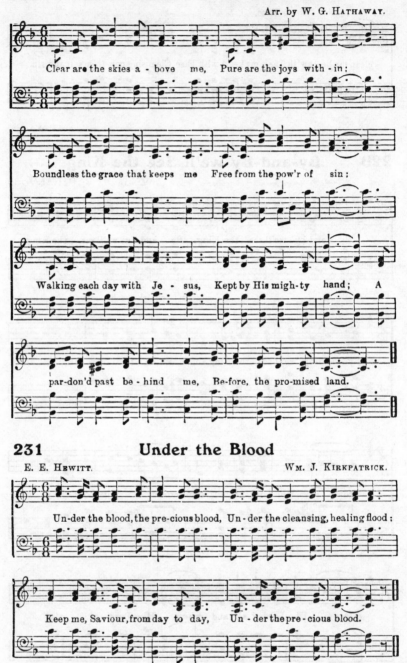

Clear are the skies a - bove me, Pure are the joys with - in;

Boundless the grace that keeps me Free from the pow'r of sin;

Walking each day with Je - sus, Kept by His migh-ty hand; A

par-don'd past be - hind me, Be-fore, the pro-mised land.

231

Under the Blood

E. E. HEWITT.

WM. J. KIRKPATRICK.

Un-der the blood, the pre-cious blood, Un - der the cleansing, healing flood;

Keep me, Saviour, from day to day, Un - der the pre - cious blood.

232   Walking with Jesus Alone

Anon.
Harmonised by W. G. HATHAWAY.

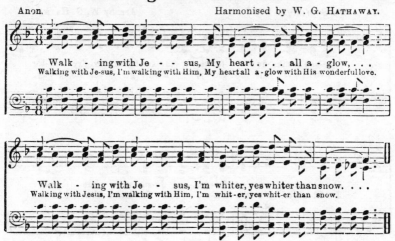

Walk - ing with Je - - sus, My heart . . . . all a - glow, . . .
Walking with Je-sus, I'm walking with Him, My heart all a-glow with His wonderful love.

Walk - ing with Je - - sus, I'm whiter, yes whiter than snow. . . .
Walking with Jesus, I'm walking with Him, I'm whit-er, yes whit-er than snow.

233   We want everybody to be Happy

Arr. by W. G. HATHAWAY.

We want ev-'ry-bo-dy to be hap-py, We want ev-'ry-bo-dy to be glad; We want ev-'ry-bo-dy to be hap-py in the Lord, And we don't want an-y-bo-dy sad.

Jesus Breaks every Fetter

Worshipfully.

Arr. by W. G. HATHAWAY.

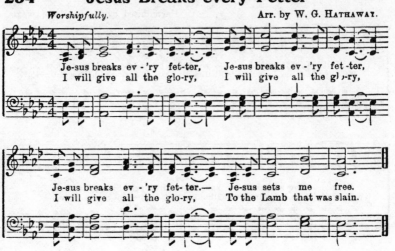

Je-sus breaks ev-'ry fet-ter,
Je-sus breaks ev-'ry fet-ter,
I will give all the glo-ry,
I will give all the glo-ry,

Je-sus breaks ev-'ry fet-ter.—
Je-sus sets me free.
I will give all the glo-ry,
To the Lamb that was slain.

Joy in Serving Jesus

REV. OSWALD J. SMITH.

B. D. ACKLEY.

There is joy, joy, Joy in serving Je-sus, Joy that throbs with-

in my heart; Ev-'ry mo-ment, ev-'ry hour, As I draw up-

on His pow'r, There is joy, joy, Joy that nev-er shall de - part.

236 Jesus will Never Fail

F. D. Byatt.
Harmony by A. E. Hayward.

F. D. B.

Je-sus will ne - ver fail,..... Je-sus will ne - ver

fail,..... Cast on Him all your care,..... He will thy

bur - dens bear;.... Je-sus will ne - ver fail,.....

Je - sus will ne - ver fail,..... Crown Him thy King for -

e - - - ver, Je-sus will ne - ver fail......

237 Isn't it Grand to be a Christian!

C. McC. and H. G. T.

CHARLOTTE McCROSSAN.
Har. by H. G. TOVEY.

1. Isn't it grand to be a Christian, Isn't it grand, (isn't it grand!)
2. Isn't it grand to live for Je - sus, Isn't it grand!
3. Isn't it grand to help your neighbour, Isn't it grand!
4. Isn't it grand to look for Je - sus, Isn't it grand!

Isn't it grand to be a Christian, Isn't it grand!
Isn't it grand to live for Je - sus, Isn't it grand!
Isn't it grand to help your neighbour, Isn't it grand!
Isn't it grand to look for Je - sus, Isn't it grand, (isn't it grand!)

Isn't it grand to be a Christ - ian, Mon-day, Tues-day, Wednesday,
Isn't it grand to live for Je - sus, Mon-day, Tues-day, Wednesday,
Isn't it grand to help your neighbour, Mon-day, Tues-day, Wednesday,
Isn't it grand to look for Je - sus, Mon-day, Tues-day, Wednesday,

Thurs-day, Fri-day, Saturday, And all day Sun-day, Isn't it grand!

238 Into My Heart

H.D.C. *Prayerfully.*

HARRY D. CLARKE

In - to my heart, In - to my heart, Come in - to my heart, Lord Je - sus;

Into my Heart (continued)

Come in to-day, Come in to stay, Come in- to my heart, Lord Je - sus.

239 I've cast my Care on Jesus

R. E. Darbagh.

B. Tetchner.

I've cast my care on Je - sus, My sym-pa-this-ing Friend, He

pro-mis'd He would guide me Thro' life un - to the end. I

put my trust in Je - sus For He will ne - ver fail, . . . He

caus-es me to tri - umph, And in His name pre - vail.

240   What the World Needs is Jesus

B.A.B.

Benj. A. Baur.

What the world needs is Je - sus, Just a glimpse of Him;

What the world needs is Je - sus, Just a glimpse of Him;

He will bring joy and glad - ness, Take a - way sin and sad - ness;

What the world needs is Je - sus, Just a glimpse of Him.

241   Oh, Hallelujah !

Slowly and worshipfully.

Arr. by W. G. H.

Oh, Hal - le - lu - jah, Oh, Hal - le - lu - jah, Thou art so love - ly and fair;

Oh, Hal - le - lu - jah, I do love Thee, Thy beau - ty is rare.

242 It's a Grand Thing to be Saved!

G. MacG.

GEORGE MacGEOCH.
Harmony by MRS. SETH SYKES.

It's a grand thing to be saved, It's a grand thing to be saved, To
know I'm safe-ly bound for heav'n, My ma-ny sins for-given; His
blood a-vails for me, From sins He set me free, It's a grand
thing, it's a grand thing, It's a grand thing to be saved.

243 Thank You for the World so Sweet

WINIFRED GINN.

Harmony by W. G. HATHAWAY.

Thank you for the world so sweet, Thank you for the food we eat;
Thank you for the birds that sing, Thank you, Lord, for ev-'ry-thing.

244 Send an S. O. S. to Jesus

SETH SYKES.

MR. & MRS. SETH SYKES.

Send an S. O. S. to Je-sus, Tell Him plainly how you feel, He's the

great-est of phy-si-cians, He can save and He can heal, Tho' you've

wandered in sin's by-ways, Tho' from Him you've gone a-stray, Send an

S. O. S. to Je-sus, He will wash your sins a-way.

245 It's So

C. E. H.

CARL E. HATCH.

Brightly.

It's so, it's so, The pow'r of God is fall-ing, As

It's so, it's so,

in, as in, As in the days of old; Look up, look

As in, as in, Look up,

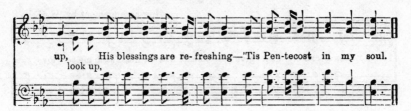

up, / look up, His blessings are re-freshing—'Tis Pen-tecost in my soul.

246　Crown Jesus King

FRANK E. ROUSH.　　　　　　　　　　　　HALDOR LILLENAS.

Crown Him! Crown Him! Highest archan-gels are sing - ing;

Crown Him! Crown Him! Heaven-ly anthems are ring - ing.

Crown Him! Crown Him! Cru-ci-fied, glo-ri-fied King!

Glo-ry to God in the high - est! E - ter-nally crown Him King!
crown Him King!

Calvary Love

New arrangement by W. G. H.

Lord cru-ci-fied, give me a heart like Thine. Teach me to love the dy-ing souls of men, And keep my heart in closest touch with Thee, And give me love, pure Calv'ry love, to bring the lost to Thee.

248

Love Lifted Me

JAMES ROWE.

HOWARD E. SMITH.

Love lift-ed me! Love lift-ed me!
e - ven me! e - ven me!

When no one but Christ could help, Love lift-ed me!

Love lift-ed me! Love lift-ed me!
e - ven me! e - ven me!

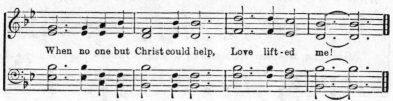

When no one but Christ could help, Love lift-ed me!

249 In my Heart a Song is Singing

L. E. DARBACH.   A. W. EDSON. Har by B. TETCHNER.

In my heart a song is sing-ing, In my heart a joy - bell ring-ing;

I've been for-giv-en, my soul is set free;

No-one knows bet-ter what this means to me, Life is a song,

I dance a - long, Sing-ing the prais-es of Je - sus.

Jesus First, Jesus Last

R. H. P.

R. Hudson Pope.

Je-sus first, Jesus last, and Je-sus all a-long, In our work, in our play, and

in our song; In the darkness, in the light, Peaceful times, or in the fight,

I am safe and all is right; For Jesus never, never fails, For Je-sus never fails.

251 · Keep the Touch of God in your Soul

M. L. H.

Mora Leonard Hatch.

Keep the touch of God in your soul, (in your soul), Keep the touch of

God in your soul, (in your soul), O wres-tle, watch and pray, Un-

til the break of day, And keep the touch of God in your soul, (in your soul).

252 To the Uttermost He Saves

J. LAWLEY.

To the ut-ter-most He saves, To the ut-ter-most He saves; Dare you
now be-lieve and His love re-ceive, To the ut-ter-most Je-sus saves.

253 O Master, Baptise Me To-day

E. C. W. BOULTON.

C. C. SWIFT.

O Mas-ter Di-vine, bap-tise me to-day, What-e-ver the
price, I'll glad-ly o-bey; Emp-ty me, hum-ble me,
fill me I pray, As all on Thy al-tar I tremblingly lay.

254   Pour Out Thy Spirit on Me

Arr. by W. G. Hathaway.

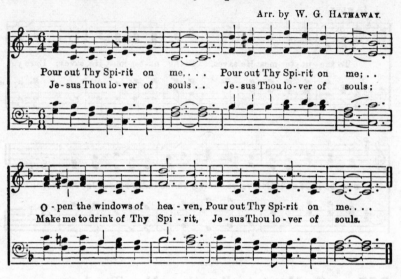

Pour out Thy Spi-rit on me,... Pour out Thy Spi-rit on me;..
Je-sus Thou lo-ver of souls.. Je-sus Thou lo-ver of souls;

O - pen the windows of hea - ven, Pour out Thy Spi-rit on me....
Make me to drink of Thy Spi - rit, Je-sus Thou lo-ver of souls.

255   The Breaking of the Day

J. W. S.

G. W. Sederquist.

O it must be the breaking of the day, O it

must be the breaking of the day... The night is al-most gone, The

day is com-ing on; O it must be the breaking of the day.

256 Wounded for Me

W.G.O.

W. G. OVENS.

Wound-ed for me! wound-ed for me! There on the cross He was wound-ed for me: Gone my trans-gres-sions, and now I am free, All be-cause Je-sus was wounded for me.

dim.

257 Wonderful Peace

B. A. B.

BENJ. A. BAUR.

Won-der-ful peace, won-der-ful peace, Wonderful peace flows o'er my soul! Purchased for me on Cal-va-ry: Won-der-ful peace of Je-sus.

258 There's Life in the Life of Jesus

Arr. W. G. HATHAWAY.

There's life in the life of Je-sus, if you live it day by day; On-ly look to Je-sus and He will lead the way. There's life e-ter-nal, life ev-er-lasting, life for ev-ermore. O glory, Hal-le-lu-jah, I'm bound for heaven's shore.

259 I'll be so Glad when Day is Done

Arr. W. G. HATHAWAY.

I'll be so glad when day is done, I'll be so glad when vic-t'ry's won. There'll be no sor-row in God's to-mor-row: I'll be so glad when Je-sus comes.

260 Joy Unspeakable

B. E. W.

B. E. WARREN.

It is joy un-speak-a-ble and full of glo-ry, Full of glo-ry,
full of glo-ry; It is joy un-speak-a-ble and full of
glo-ry, Oh, the half has ne-ver yet been told.

261 New Days

F. M. L.

F. M. LEHMAN.
Har. by MRS. C. LEHMAN MAYS.

O the bless-ed new days, Now are mine; I am in His
keep-ing, Shade or shine. Bask-ing in the ful-ness,
Lost in praise; Out of dark-ness in-to light—Glad new days.

I'm on the Sunny Side

C. F. W.

C. F. WEIGELE.

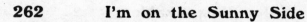

I'm on the sunny side, I'm on the sunny side, I'm on the sunny side of life;

I'm on the sunny side, I'm on the sunny side, I'm on the sunny side of life.

Christ's Own Peace

COLIN STERNE.

H. ERNEST NICHOL, Mus. BAC., OXON.

Light that groweth not pale With day's de - crease,

Love that nev-er can fail Till life shall cease;

Joy no tri-al can mar, Hope that shineth a-far,

Faith se - rene as a star, And Christ's own peace.

264   Good Morning to Heaven

W. C. Poole.

C. Austin Miles.

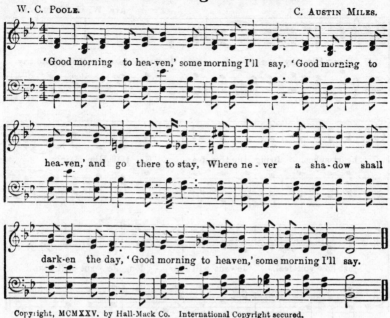

'Good morning to hea-ven,' some morning I'll say, 'Good morning to hea-ven,' and go there to stay, Where ne-ver a sha-dow shall dark-en the day, 'Good morning to heaven,' some morning I'll say.

265   Romans Ten and Nine

Thos. R. Cupples.

Ro-mans ten and nine is a fav'rite verse of mine, Con-fessing Christ as Lord, I am saved by grace di - vine, These precious words of pro-mise in gold-en let-ters shine, Ro - mans ten and nine.

Bring Him Thy Sorrows

Arr. W. G. HATHAWAY.

Bring Him thy sor-rows, Bring Him thy tears; Bring Him thy

heart-aches, Bring Him thy fears. Go tell Him plainly

just how you feel, Je-sus will par - don, Je-sus will heal.

267

Hallelujah! I am Free

E. C. W. BOULTON.

C. C. SWIFT.

Allegro moderato.

Hal - le - lu - jah! now I'm free; All my bur - dens roll'd on

Thee; And my soul is fill'd with praise, As I jour-ney through the

days; Grace and strength Thou dost re-new, Whilst the goal I keep in

Hallelujah! I am Free—*continued*

view, soon the prize I shall pos-sess, Reign with Thee in righteous

rall.

ness. Hal-le-lu - - - jah! Hal-lu-lu - - - jah!

268 My Lord Abides

Slowly. Arr. W. G. HATHAWAY.

My Lord a - bides, my Lord a- bides; And in His strength my weakness

hides. I'll trust in Him whate'er be-tides: My precious Lord a - bides.

269 I walk with the King

JAMES ROWE. B. D. ACKLEY.

I walk with the King, Hal-le - lu - jah, I walk with the King, praise His name

No long-er I roam, my soul fa-ces home, I walk and I talk with the King.

270 I Fell in Love with Jesus

T. K.

THOS. KEMP.

I fell in love with Je - sus, I fell in love with Je - sus;

rall.

Wonderful day of re - joic - ing When I fell in love with my Lord.

271 All Hail the Power

EDWARD PERRONET. *cres.* HAYDN.

mf

All hail the pow'r of Je - su's name, Let an - gels pros-trate fall;
Bring forth the roy - al di - a - dem, And crown Him Lord of all.

p

And crown Him Lord of all, ... And crown Him Lord of all, ...

mf

Bring forth the roy - al di - a - dem, Bring forth the roy - al

pp *mf*

di - a - dem, And crown Him Lord, And crown Him Lord of all.

272 **Since Jesus came to Stay**

Fistoria Mieler.   Charlie D. Tillman.

I bless the hap-py day When Je-sus came to stay, And tho' my sins were
crimson red, He's taken them all a - way, And by His mighty power, He's
chang'd my night to day, And now I've a life that's fill'd with joy, Since Jesus came to stay.

273 **Joy! Joy! Joy!**

Joy! Joy! Joy! with joy my heart is ring - ing; Joy! Joy! Joy! His
love to me is known; My sins are all for - gi - ven, I'm on my way to
hea - ven; My heart is bub-bling o - ver with His Joy! Joy! Joy!

274   Jesus, How Wonderful

EINAR ECKBERG & J. GILES.   W. R. HUTTON.

Je - sus how won-derful Thy love has prov'd to be, E'en in our
darkest hour Thou ga - vest li - ber-ty; Guide us a -long life's way,
clo - ser to Thee we pray, Till on that crowning day we meet with Thee.

275   Ever Near to bless and Cheer

Arranged by REV. TOM JONES.

Ev - er near to bless and cheer In the darkest hour; When I'm
tempt-ed I can feel His power. At His side I'll a - bide, Ne - ver
more to roam, Till at last, Fighting past, He will take me home.

Over the Jasper Sea

The congregation should be divided into two sections, one taking the 1st and the other the 2nd chorus, both being sung together.

Arr. by W. G. HATHAWAY.

1ST CHORUS.

O - ver and o - ver, Like a might - y sea,

2ND CHORUS.

Over the sea, Over the sea, Je - sus, Sa - viour, pi - lot me,

PIANO.

Comes the love of Je - sus Roll - ing o - ver me.

O - ver the sea, O - ver the sea, O - ver the jas - per sea (jasper sea).

It is Lovely

It is love-ly! It is love-ly! All my sins are washed a - way, All my sins are washed a - way.

278 Stay Still in the Hand of the Potter

Anon.

FRANCIS WALKER.

Stay still in the hand of the Pot-ter; Lie low 'neath His wonder-ful touch;

He shapeth and mouldeth in mer-cy The clay that He lov-eth so much.

Sur - ren - der thy-self to His workings, The curve and the hol-low He wills;

rit.

Nor shrink from the pain and the pressure, For the vessel He fashions He fills.

279 God is so Good to Me

L.S.L.

LIDA SHIVERS LEECH.

God is so good to me (to me), God is so good to me (to me),

I'll love and serve Him faith-ful-ly, He is so good to me (to me).

280 Dwelling in Beulah Land

C.A.M.

C. AUSTIN MILES.

I'm liv-ing on the mountain, un-der-neath a cloud-less

sky, Praise God! I'm drinking at the fountain that nev-er shall run

dry, O yes! I'm feast-ing on the man-na from a boun-ti-ful sup-

ply For I am dwell-ing in Beu-lah Land.

Arranged by W. G. HATHAWAY.

High, higher than the hill-tops, Deep, deeper than the sea;

Wide, wider than the o - cean Is Je-sus's love to me, Hal-le-lu - jah,

Once I was a sin - ner, Sunk in sin and shame, Till the

love of God laid hold on me, O praise His ho - ly name.

282   A Jubilee

T. H. arr.

Arr. by THORO HARRIS.

I have a ju - bi - lee with-in my heart, A rap-ture that can

ne - ver-more de - part; Since Christ hath set me free, I'm

hap - py as can be, I have a ju - bi - lee with-in my heart.

283 I Fell in Love with the Nazarene

I fell in love with the Nazarene, The beau-ti-ful Na - za - rene, Whose

face with glo - ry was a-light, The fairest my eyes have seen.

Near His side I would a - bide, With ne - ver a veil be - tween,

Since I fell so deep in love With Je-sus, the Na - za - rene.

Jesus has Won my Heart

J.H.

J. HODGSON.

I find in Je - sus my Sa - viour, Something I once ne - ver

knew, .. Something that tells me He guides me, Loves me and

cares for me too; . . . I know my sins are for - giv - en,

From Him I'll ne'er de - part, ... Je - sus came in and

took all my sin, Now He has won my heart . . . . .

285

Room at the Fountain

M. J. H.

MRS. M. J. HARRIS.

Room, room, yes, there is room, Room at the fountain for thee, (for thee);

Room, room, yes, there is room, There's room at the fountain for thee.

286   ## Back to the Bible

R. E. DARRAGH.   A. W. EDSOR. (Harmonised.)

Let the call go forth to the ends of the earth, Back to the grand old

Bi - - ble. Lift the stand-ard high for the truth dare die,

Back to the grand old Bi - - ble. Bold-ly stand for the right, tho'

fierce be the fight, But from the truth ne - ver fal - ter.

Won-der-ful Word, Glo - ri - ous Word. Back to the grand old Bi - ble.

Jesus my Saviour

F. D. B.   F. D. BYATT.

Je - sus my Sa - viour, Dear-er than all to me; .... Sweet rose of Sha - - ron, Man of Cal - va - ry, ... Draw me still clos - er to Thy lov - ing breast, ... For in Thy pre - - sence my soul is blest. ....

288 **After the Shadows**

James Rowe.

Samuel W. Beazley.

After the sha - dows, there will be sun - shine; After the
After the sha-dows, there will be sun-shine,

frown, the soul-cheering smile; .. Cling to the Sa - viour,
After the frown, the soul-cheering, soul-cheering smile; Cling to the Saviour,

love Him for - ev - er; All will be well in a lit-tle while.
love Him for-ev - er;

289 **Sweet Will of God**

Mabel Craig.

Harmony by Marjorie Mileham.

M. C.

With expression.

Sweet will of God be thou my por - tion, Self lost in

thee my heart can re - joice; If in the val - ley

or on the moun-tain, Sweet will of God my choice.

He Sought me, He Found me

C.P.D.

CYRIL P. DAWES.

I am e - ver so glad that He sought me, He sought me, He
ve-ry, ve-ry glad, ve-ry, very glad

sought me, I am e - ver so glad that He sought me, To
ve-ry, ve-ry glad, ve-ry, very glad To

make me His ve - ry own; From the glo-ry of heaven He
From the glo - ry
His ve-r-y own;

Marcato.
ff

will-ing - ly came, Thinking not of Himself but my sinning and shame, I am
Je - sus came, Think-ing of my sin and shame,

e - ver so glad that He found me, And made me His ve - ry own.

ELIM PUBLISHING COMPANY, LTD., CLAPHAM CRESCENT, LONDON, S.W.4—20919

Elim Choruses No. 6

291   As I walked through the Land

Jean Wilson.
Andante. Dolce.

Ernest P. Grahame.

As I walked thro' the land With the Book in my hand, The land where my Saviour had died; . . . As I walked thro' His land With His Book in my hand Oh, I thought of Him cru-ci-fied! . . . His vir-gin birth, His sin-less life, His won-der-ful ris-ing a-gain! . . As I walked thro' the land With the Book in my hand, I thought of Him com-ing to reign.

292   I was There when it Happened

H.J.L.

HERBERT J. LACEY.

I was there when it happen'd, and I ought to know; His Spirit burning
in me, set my heart a - glow; So I praise the Lord to-day, He has
wash'd my sins a - way; I was there when it happen'd, and I ought to know.

293   Wonderful Friend, Mine to the End

D.B.G.

DOUGLAS B. GRAY.

Slowly. con espress.

Won - der-ful Friend, mine to the end, Sweet a - dor -
a - tion from hearts now as - cend, Lead - ing me, guid - ing me,
day un - to day, Won - der - ful Friend, mine to the end.

294 **Saviour, I would Worship Thee**

Mr. and Mrs. SETH SYKES.

Saviour, I would wor-ship Thee, My soul is
fill'd with ec-sta-sy, That Thou should'st die for me on Cal-va-
ry, Saviour, I would wor-ship Thee.

295 **O Jesus, Draw Me**

Air by F. M. THOMPSON.
Harmony by W. G. HATHAWAY.

F.M.T.

O Je-sus, draw me, Dear Lord, just draw me in-to a
clos-er walk with Thee, O let me feel Thee For-e-ver
near me: I long to know Thee more, and more, and more.

296 My Burden of Sin Rolled Away

Mr. and Mrs. S. Sykes.

My burden of sin roll'd a - way, a -way, My burden of sin roll'd a - way;

I'm ever so happy because I am free, My burden of sin rolled a - way.

297 Lead Me to some Soul To-day

Will H. Houghton.

Wendell P. Loveless.

Lead me to some soul to - day, O teach me, Lord, just what to say;

Friends of mine are lost in sin, And can - not find their way.

Few there are who seem to care, And few there are who pray; who pray;

Melt my heart and fill my life, Give me one soul to - day.

298 ## Wonderful Love

THORO HARRIS, arr.

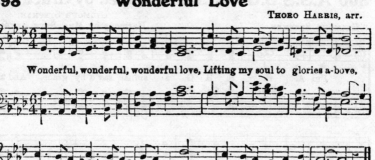

Wonderful, wonderful, wonderful love, Lifting my soul to glories a-bove,

Filling me, thrilling me day by day: O it was wonderful love!

299 ## Thou art the Potter

Air by FRANCES MORRISON.
Harmony by AUDREY WITTS.

FRANCES MORRISON.

Solo in the underpart.

Thou art the Pot-ter, I am the clay, Break me and

melt me, Mould me I pray, In-to Thine i-mage,

From self set free, That I may e-ver, Thy chan-nel be.

300 A.S.S.B.G.—A Sinner Saved by Grace

Gilmour Stephen.

Gilmour Stephen,
Harmony by Mrs. Seth Sykes.

I'm A. S. S. B. G. a sinner sav'd by grace, And the
Lord has gone to pre-pare for me a place; John three
six-teen is my knowledge, And the Bi-ble is my col-lege, I'm an
A. S. S. B. G. a sin-ner sav'd by grace.

301 If I but Touch His Seamless Dress

P. Le Tissier.

Arr. by P. A. Ruchon.

If I but touch His seam-less dress, I shall be blest.

Though surging crowds a-round Him press I shall find rest.

302 The Cross it Standeth Fast

HORATIUS BONAR.   JAMES McGRANAHAN.

Hal-le-lu-jah, hal-le-lu-jah. hal-le-lu-jah for the Cross,

Hal-le-lu-jah, hal-le-lu-jah, it shall ne-ver suf-fer loss!

303

I was Glad

Harmonised by E. P. GRAHAME.

I was glad when they said un-to me, Let us

go in-to the house of the Lord. I was glad when they
(I was glad)

said, Let us go in-to the house of the Lord.
(when they said,)

304 **They Come**

Thoro Harris, tr.   Russell DeKoven, harmonized by Douglas B. Gray.

Since Je-sus has set me free, My heart is so full of glee; No longer I bear the bur-den of care, His yoke is so sweet to me. My soul was as black as night, But darkness has tak-en flight; Now I have the vic-to-ry, For Je-sus has set me free.

305 **Mine at Last!**

James Rowe.

Mine at last! mine at last! Je-sus has hid-den my wayward past, Heard my plea, made me free; Je-sus is mine at last.

306 Can you wonder at the People?

Arr. by MISS M. HONEYSETT.

With spirit.

Can you won - der at the peo - ple be - ing en - vious, When they see that we're as hap - py as can be, For the glo - ry of the Lord is all a - round us, We're as hap - py as the birds up - on the tree. Hal - le - lu - jah, Hal - le - lu - jah, Hal - le lu - jah, for my sins are all for - giv'n, Ve - ry pre - cious is Je - sus, And my heart's a lit - tle 'Hal - le - lu - jah heav'n.'

307 There's a Shout in the Camp

C.A.M.

C. Austin Miles.

There's a shout in the camp, Hal-le - lu - jah! Glo - ry to God!

There's an e - cho in heav'n, Hal-le - lu - jah! Glo - ry to God!

308 O, it is Jesus

Arr. R. W. Oliver.

O, it is Je - sus, Yes, it is Je - sus, O, it is

O, it is Je - sus, O, yes, it is Je - sus,

Je - sus in my soul; For I have touch'd the

Je - sus, Je - sus in my soul, in my soul;

hem of His gar - ment, And His blood has made me whole.

309

Jesus Only

ARTHUR S. BOOTH-CLIBBORN.

Arr. from VERDI.

If . . . . I have Je-sus on - - ly, Can . . . . I be

e - ver lone - - ly? If He suf-fice me, what can en-

tice me from Him a-way? With Him I stay, for aye, for aye!

310

My Burdens Rolled away

MRS. MINNIE A. STEELE.

Roll'd a - way, roll'd a - way, I am hap-py since my
rolled a-way, rolled a-way,

bur-dens rolled a - way; Roll'd a - way, roll'd a-
since my bur-dens rolled a - way; rolled a-way,

way, I am hap-py since my bur-dens roll'd a - way.

Precious Hiding Place

Avis B. Christiansen.

Wendell P. Loveless.

Pre - cious hid - ing place Pre - cious hid - ing place, In the
shel - ter of His love; Not a doubt or fear, Since my
rit.
Lord is near, And I'm shel - tered in His love.

312 Just Smile and keep on Smiling

T.J. *Brightly.*

Rev. Tom Jones.

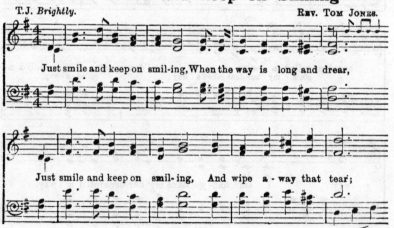

Just smile and keep on smil-ing, When the way is long and drear,

Just smile and keep on smil-ing, And wipe a - way that tear;

Just Smile and keep on Smiling (*continued*)

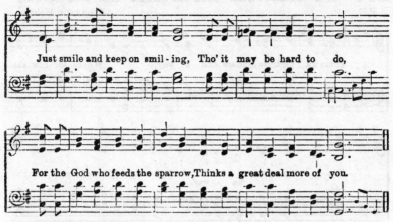

Just smile and keep on smil - ing, Tho' it may be hard to do,

For the God who feeds the sparrow, Thinks a great deal more of you.

313   # Win Them One by One

C.A.M. *In march time.*   C. Austin Miles.

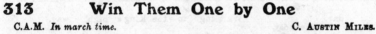

{ So, you bring the one next to you,   And I'll bring the one next to me;
{ If you'll bring the one next to you,   And I bring the one next to me;

1st time only.

In all kinds of weather, we'll all work together, And see what can be done;

2nd time only.

In no time at all we'll have them all, So win them, win them one by one.

314 We shall see the Desert as the Rose

F.H.

FLORENCE HORTON.

There's a high-way there and a way, Where sor-row shall
and a way,
flee a - way, And the light shines bright as the
flee a - way,
day, Walk-ing in the King's high - way.
as the day,

315 Sorrows of Satan

J. SOUTAR.

Harmonised by LIZZIE THOMSON.

I'm glad Sa-tan's sor-ry, he's sor-ry I'm glad, He oft was so hap-py when

I was so sad; He de-light-ed to think I was one of his own, But

I'm pleas'd to say he's mis-tak-en. For I am so hap-py to

know I am free, And Sa-tan no long-er has pow'r o-ver me; While trusting in

Je - sus, I know I shall be Counted one of the sor-rows of Sa - tan.

316   **Love found a Way**

CONSTANCE B. RIED.   HARRY DIXON LOES.

Love found a way .... to re - deem my soul, ...
a way   to re - deem my soul,

Love found a way .... that could make me whole; ...
a way   could make me whole;

Love sent my Lord .... to the cross of shame, ..
my Lord   to the cross of shame.

ad lib.

Love found a - way, O praise His ho - ly name!

317 I'll Praise His Name

C.P.D.

CYRIL P. DAWES.

I'll praise His name for e - ver - more, I'll praise His name for ev - er - more, I'll praise His name, praise His name, praise His name and praise, I'll praise His name for ev - er - more.

praise

318 I've been Redeemed

Arr. by GEO. W. COOKE.

I've been re - deemed . . . . by the blood of the Lamb, ...
I've been re - deem'd
the dy - ing Lamb

I've been re - deemed . . . by the blood of the Lamb, ...
I've been re-deem'd
the Lamb of God,

I've been Redeemed (continued)

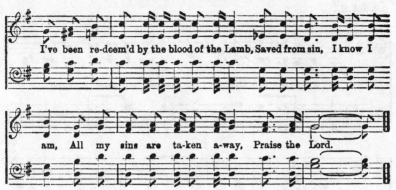

I've been re-deem'd by the blood of the Lamb, Saved from sin, I know I

am, All my sins are ta-ken a-way, Praise the Lord.

319   There'll be Showers of Blessing

Mrs. C. H. Morris.

Tithes of love and will-ing ser - vice, Tithes of sil - ver and of

gold; When the tithes .... are ga-thered in, When the
when the tithes   gathered in.

tithes .... are ga-ther'd in, There'll be blessings more than we
When the tithes   gathered in,

can con - tain, When the tithes .... are ga-thered in.
When the tithes are   ga - thered in.

A.E.A.H.

Andante ed doloroso.

A. E. A. HAYWARD.

In   this world of woe   Few   folk seem to   know

Where to turn, which road   to   take. . . . .   Life to some may

seem   One   long hor-rid dream,   With   no hope when

they   a - wake. . . . . .   Bright - en their I -

deas,   Ban - ish all their fears;   Tell how Christ, in won - drous

love, ... Suf-fer'd grief and pain; Died, but rose a-

gain To prepare a Home a-bove.

321 Wondrous Saviour

RUTH DEBBETT.   W. G. HATHAWAY.

I have a Sa-viour, a won-drous Sa-viour, And He is

all in all to me; He's e-ver near me to help and

cheer me, And He has pro-mised He'll take me through.

322 My Sins are Blotted out I Know

Arr. by W. G. HATHAWAY.

Alla marcia.

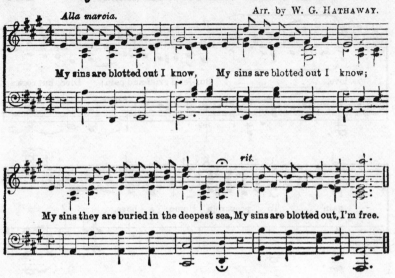

My sins are blotted out I know, My sins are blotted out I know;

rit.

My sins they are buried in the deepest sea, My sins are blotted out, I'm free.

323 Pray Through

SETH SYKES.

Pray through, pray thro', What-ev-er you do; Do not be dis-

courag'd, God will an-swer you; In life's deepest myst'ries, You will

sure-ly find the clue; Don't be dis-cour-aged, pray through.

Like a Mighty Sea

324. Like a Mighty Sea

Clarence B. Strouse.

H. L. Gilmour.

Like a might-y sea, Like a might-y sea, Comes the love of Je - sus sweep-ing o - ver me; The waves of glo - ry roll, the shouts I can't con-trol, Comes the love of Je - sus sweeping o'er my soul.

325. Keep the Music Ringing

E. E. Hewitt.

Wm. J. Kirkpatrick.

Keep....... the mu - sic ring-ing all the way,
Keep the mu - sic ring-ing,

Serve..... the Lord with gladness ev-'ry day, Keep the mu-sic ringing,
Serve the Lord with gladness,

Keep the mu-sic ring-ing, Keep the mu-sic ringing all the way.......
ring-ing, ringing all the way.

Satisfied

A. H. ACKLEY.

B. D. ACKLEY.

I . . . . shall be sat - is - fied, I I
I shall be sat - is - fied, I shall be sat - is - fied, I shall be sat -

shall be sat - is - fied; Shel-tered a - bove by His
is - fied. I shall be sat - is - fied;

rit.

in - fi - nite love, I shall be sat - is - - fied. . . .

Just when I need Him most

E.H.G.S.

E. H. G. SARGENT.

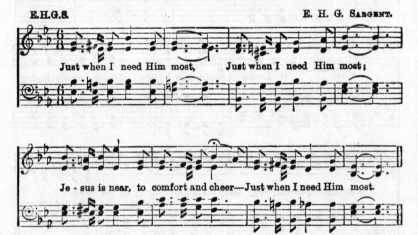

Just when I need Him most, Just when I need Him most;

Je - sus is near, to comfort and cheer—Just when I need Him most.

328   I'm running up the Shining Way

arr. by W. G. HATHAWAY.

I'm running up the shining way, I'm running up the shining way. His

glory fills my soul, While the hallelujahs roll, I'm running up the shining way.

329   Jesus loves the 'Whosoever'

J. FINDLAY (Greenock).   C. C. CONVERSE.

Je-sus loves the 'whoso-e-ver,'   Of what-e-ver land they be;

And He gently calls them to Him,   To sal-vation full and free:

All the folks from bonnie Scot-land,   And those from the English dales,

Not for-get-ting dear old Ire-land,   And the rugged hills of Wales.

330 The Joy of Yielding

E. C. W. BOULTON. *Moderato.* A. R. G. WITTS.

O the wondrous joy of yield - ing To each new command of Thine,

Giv-ing ut-termost o - be - dience, To the claims of love di - vine,

Plunging deeper, ev - er deep - er In - to Love's resistless tide,

Carried onward to the o - cean, Ev-'ry moment sat-is - fied.

331 He Ransomed Me

JULIA H. JOHNSTON. J. W. HENDERSON.

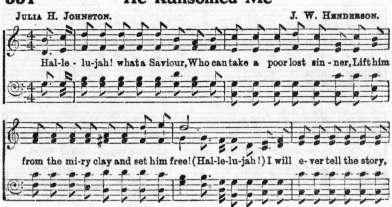

Hal - le - lu-jah! what a Saviour, Who can take a poor lost sin - ner, Lift him

from the mi-ry clay and set him free! (Hal-le-lu-jah!) I will e - ver tell the story,

He Ransomed Me (*continued*)

ad lib.

Shouting Glo-ry, glo-ry, glo-ry, Hal-le-lu-jah! Je-sus lift-ed me.

332 There's a Foursquare Gospel Revival

R. E. DARRAGH.

DOREEN TODD.

There's a Foursquare Gospel re-vi-val Sweeping the world to-

day, . . . Giv-ing it joy and glad-ness, No matter what

peo-ple say; Meeting the need of the mass-es, A

need which nothing can fill . . . But Je-sus the Sa-viour,

Je-sus the Heal-er, Bap-ti-ser, com-ing King.

333   Everybody Ought to Love Him!

H.M. & I.M.P.

H. MITCHELL & I. McPHERSON.

Ev-'ry-bo-dy ought to love Him, ev-'ry-bo-dy ev'-ry-where;

Ev-'ry-bo-dy ought to love Him, He will banish ev-'ry care;

He's the Author of sal-va-tion; condemna-tion He did bear;

Jesus died for ev'ry na-tion, ev-ry-bo-dy ev-'ry-where.

334   Balm in Gilead

Largo, ad lib.

Arr. by W. G. HATHAWAY.

There is a balm in Gil-e-ad, To make the wounded whole;

There is a balm in Gil-e-ad To heal the sin-sick soul.

Let's all Join together

R. E. Darragh.

A. W. E. Hayward.

Let's all join to - ge - ther In prais-ing the name of the Lord, Let's all join to - ge - ther In spreading His fame a - broad; Lifting our voic-es in song, Praising Him all the day long; Let's all join to - ge - ther In prais-ing the name of the Lord.

336 Everybody Happy? Say Amen!

MRS. BERNICE S. EVANS.

Ev-'ry-bo-dy hap-py? Say A-men! Ev-'ry-bo-dy hap-py? Say A-men! Joy and peace are mul-ti-plied, Now that Je-sus is our guide: Ev-'ry-bo-dy hap-py? Say A-men!

337 I took a Plunge in the Crimson Flood

MR. & MRS. SETH SYKES.

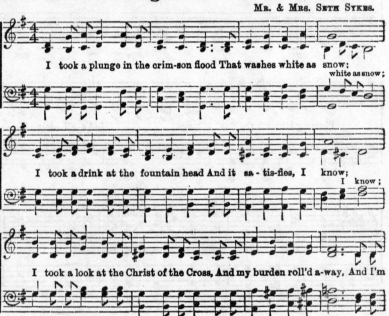

I took a plunge in the crim-son flood That washes white as snow; white as snow;

I took a drink at the fountain head And it sa-tis-fies, I know; I know;

I took a look at the Christ of the Cross, And my burden roll'd a-way, And I'm

I took a Plunge in the Crimson Flood (*continued*)

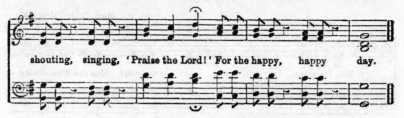

shouting, singing, 'Praise the Lord!' For the happy, happy day.

338   How Precious is He!

W. ROGERS.

How precious is He, . . . So precious to me; . . .

Jesus my comfort, my strength and my stay, He is the Life, and the Truth, and the

Way. What rapture 'twill be, . . When Jesus I see; In

Him I'm confiding, and e - ver a-bid-ing, For how precious is He! . . .

339 ## Back to Pentecost

Mrs. C. H. Morris.

Has He come to you, to you, to you? Has the Com-for-ter
come to you? (to you?) The Lord will re-prove the
world of sin, When the Com-fort-er comes to you (to you).

340 ## Chorus Medley

Arr. by W. G. Hathaway.

The Old, Old Sto-ry, it is ev-er new, The Old, Old Sto-ry,
praise the Lord 'tis true, That Je-sus died for me as well as you,—

Chorus Medley *(continued)*

I love the Old, Old Sto - ry. When the roll . . . is called up yon - der, I'll be walk-ing in the King's high - way, Tell me the Old, Old Sto - ry, I love Him bet-ter ev - 'ry day, Hal - le - lu - jah. 'I will make you fish-ers of men, if you on - ly fol - low Me!' Now none but Christ can sat - is - fy, And there's no o - ther Name for me.

341 Swing Wide the Door of your Heart

Arr. by W. G. HATHAWAY.

Swing wide the door of your heart to the King of kings,

Bid Him en - ter, Wonder-ful peace He brings,

He will shelt - er you un - der His outstretch'd wings,

Swing wide the door of your heart to the King of kings.

342   Crucified

F.A.J.

FREDERICK A. JACOBSEN.

Sing slowly and reverently. | 1st time. || 2nd time.

{ Cru-cified on Cal-vary, My Saviour bled and died for me; }
{ Cru-cified on Cal-va-ry, To save my soul and (*Omit*........) } set me free.

ELIM PUBLISHING COMPANY, LTD., CLAPHAM CRESCENT, LONDON, S.W.4.—19886

Elim Choruses No. 7

Altogether Lovely

W.P.L.

WENDELL P. LOVELESS.

Al - to-geth - er love - ly, He is al - to-geth - er love - ly, And the fair - est of ten thou - sand, This won-der-ful Friend di - vine; He gave Himself to save me, Now He lives in heav'n to keep me, He is al - to-geth - er love - ly, Is this wonderful Saviour of mine.

344 I've been Lifted out of the Miry Clay

S.S.

MR. & MRS. SETH SIKES.

I've been lift - ed out of the mi - ry clay,

I've been lift - ed, I'm on the Rock to stay (to stay), A

song of praise to God I sing, For Je - sus makes the joy-bells ring,

I've been lift - ed out of the mi - ry clay.

345 Till You Know Jesus

W.P.L.

WENDELL P. LOVELESS.

May be sung as a Duet, or all voices in Unison.

You'll never know real peace till you know Jesus, No mat-ter how or

where you try,............ For life is but loss with-out Him,

Till You know Jesus *(continued)*

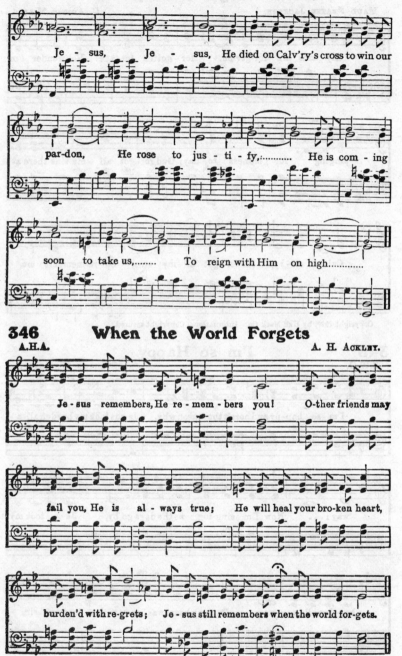

Je - sus, Je - sus, He died on Calv'ry's cross to win our

par-don, He rose to jus - ti - fy,............ He is com - ing

soon to take us,......... To reign with Him on high..............

346   When the World Forgets

A.H.A.

A. H. ACKLEY.

Je - sus remembers, He re - mem - bers you! O-ther friends may

fail you, He is al - ways true; He will heal your bro-ken heart,

burden'd with re-grets; Je - sus still remembers when the world for-gets.

347 God Forgot all my Sins

MAUD FRAZER JACKSON.

C. AUSTIN MILES.

My sins are for-giv-en, for-gotten for aye! No wonder I'm singing for gladness to-day; God for-got all my sins there at Cal - va-ry, He for-got all my sins, but re-members me.

348 I'm so Happy

S. W. G.

STANTON W. GAVITT.

I'm so hap-py and here's the reason why, Je-sus took my burden all a-way; ... Now I'm sing-ing as the days go by, Je-sus took my bur-den all a - way. Once my heart was heavy with a load of sin,

Je-sus took the load and gave me peace within; Now I'm hap-py and

that's the rea-son why, Je-sus took my bur-den all a - way.

349   Wonderful, Wonderful Jesus!

B.A.B.

Slowly and adoringly.

BENJAMIN A. BAUR.

Won-der-ful, won-der-ful Je - sus! Who can compare with Thee!..

Wonderful, wonderful Je - sus! Fair-er than all art Thou to me....

a tempo.   *rit.*   *ffz*

Won-der-ful, won-der-ful Je - sus! Oh, how my soul loves Thee!

Fair - er than all the fair - est, Je-sus, art Thou to me!

350 Christ, the Hope of the World

H.G.T.

HERBERT G. TOVEY.

Christ, the hope of the world, ... Christ, the hope of the world, ...
(light) the world, (light) the world,

All vic-to-ri-ous, e-ver glo-ri-ous, He lives for us to-day.... The
to-day,

Saviour we love is a faithful guide, And walking each moment close by my side,

He is inviting you, Welcome He offers you, Christ, the hope of the world.
(light) the world.

351 Cleanse Me

J. EDWIN ORR.

arr. by JACK WRIGHT.

O Ho - ly Ghost, ... Re - vi - val comes from

PIANO.

8ve.

Cleanse Me (*continued*)

Thee:... Send a re-vi-val— Start the work in me:.......... Thy Word de-clares.... Thou wilt sup-ply our need:.... For bless-ing now, O Lord, I hum--bly plead....

352 **Christ Changes Not**

A.S.H. ALICE S. HEINZ.

He's the same to-day as yes-ter-day, He chang-es not;

He's the same to-day as yes-ter-day, He chang-es not;

Though the world may change and kingdoms fall, He's the Rock of A - ges,

All in All, Yes-ter-day, to-day and for - e - ver, Christ chang-es not.

353 **Christ is Mine**

W.P.L. WENDELL P. LOVELESS.

What tho' the skies be dark and drea-ry, Christ is mine; yes, mine;

What tho' my heart be worn and wea-ry, Christ is mine. yes, mine.

Christt is Mine (continued)

He fills my life with joy and peace, And hope di - vine; He is my Sa - viour, Mas-ter, Comforter and Keep-er, Christ is mine.

354 In the Morning

N.J.C.

NORMAN J. CLAYTON.

We shall see Him in the morn-ing, When the clouds have roll'd a - way;

We shall meet Him at the dawn-ing Of a ne - ver-end-ing day;

Ev -'ry tri - al will be end - ed, And the cross - es all laid by;

When we see the face of Je - sus, In the mansions of the sky.

I'm Saved, Saved, Saved

CHARLOTTE McCROSSAN.
Harmony by HERBERT G. TOVEY.

C.McC.

I'm saved, saved, saved. . . My sins are all ta-ken a-

way. . . I'm saved, saved, saved, . . And hap-py in

Je-sus each day; . . He's ta-ken a-way all the bur-den of sin, The

bloodstream from Cal-va-ry cleans-es with-in, And now I can

shout, For there's nev-er a doubt That I'm saved, saved, saved.

All that I Need is Jesus

D.M.A. and GLADYS TOMKINS.　　　　　　　　　　DON M. ALLEN.

All that I need is Je - sus, All that I need is Je - - sus; For He so wondrously sat - is - fies, All my ev - 'ry need sup - plies. All that I need is Je - sus, All that I need is Je - - sus; When I am tempt-ed I know He is near, All that I need is Je - sus.

E. C. W. BOULTON.

Adagio e molto espress.

DOUGLAS B. GRAY.

Spi - rit di - vine, O quick-en us now, Whilst in Thy

pre - sence, hum - bly we bow, Set all our hearts a

rit. rall.

blaze with Thy love, Teach us the se - cret of life from a - bove.

358   **Near to the Heart of God**

C. B. McAFEE.

There is a place of qui - et rest, Near to the heart of God,

A place where sin can - not mo-lest, Near to the heart of God.

O Je - sus, blest Re - deem - er, Sent from the heart of God,

Hold us, who wait be-fore Thee, Near to the heart of God.

359 ## The Saviour and Keeper

A.P.G.
ALFRED P. GIBBS, Har. by EDNA LOTZ.

The Saviour will keep you, not only on Sunday, But each day the whole jour-

through! On Monday and Tuesday and Wen'sday and Thursday and

Friday and Saturday too! Each day of the week, and each week of the

month, And each month of the year He'll be true, So trust Him, con-

fess Him, And serve and o-bey Him, He'll save, keep and satisfy you!

360

Under Thy Sway, Lord!

G.E.J.F.

C. H. M. FOSTER

Under Thy sway Lord, under Thy sway, Jesus the conqueror, have Thine own way;

Fashion me, make me strong for the fray, Always vic-to-ri-ous un-der Thy sway.

361

Sweeter than the Day before

ROBERT C. LOVELESS.

WENDELL P. LOVELESS.

Ev-'ry day with Je-sus   Is sweeter than the day be-fore,
Ev-'ry day with Je-sus,   Sweet-er than be-

Ev-'ry day with Je-sus,   I love Him more and more;
fore.   Ev-'ry day with Je-sus,   Love Him more and

Je-sus saves and keeps me,   And He's the One I'm waiting for;
more;   Je-sus saves and keeps me,   I am wait-ing;

Ev-'ry day with Je-sus   Is sweeter than the day be-fore.

FAY WALLINFORD.   DON M. ALLEN.

God   hears and He   an - swers pray'r ;   Cast   on Je-sus your

ev - 'ry care,   Trust in His prom-is - es, They cannot fail,

For with the Fa - ther He'll ev - er pre-vail.   God   hears and He

an-swers pray'r, Frees my spi - rit from all de-spair.   Has-ten to

take Him your prob-lems, For God   an - swers   prayer.........

363 **Through every Day**

W.P.L. *Not too fast.* WENDELL P. LOVELESS.

Thro' ev-'ry day He watch-es o'er me, Thro' ev'ry day He cares;
He cares;

Thro' ev-'ry day He leads and guides me, Burdens and griefs He

bears; Thro' ev'ry day I love to serve Him, Pleasures of earth grow
glad-ly bears;

dim; Thro' ev'ry day, each glo-ri-ous day with Him.

364 **Cheer up, ye Saints of God**

Cheer up ye saints of God, There's nothing to worry a - bout;

Nothing to make you feel a - fraid, Nothing to make you doubt; Re -

Cheer up, ye Saints of God (*continued*)

mem- ber Je - sus nev - er fails, So why not trust Him and shout, You'll be

sor-ry you worried at all, To-mor-row morn - . . . ing.

365   **Keep Praising**

W.P.L.   WENDELL P. LOVELESS.

Keep praising, keep praising, When the days are dark and drear; Keep

and drear;

prais-ing, keep prais-ing, God will guide you, ne - ver fear; Keep

ne-ver fear;

prais -ing, keep prais-ing, Thankful hearts to Him be rais-ing; Has the

Lord not said, There is glo-ry on a-head—So keep on prais - ing Him.

366 The Old Rugged Cross

G. B.

Rev. Geo. Bennard.

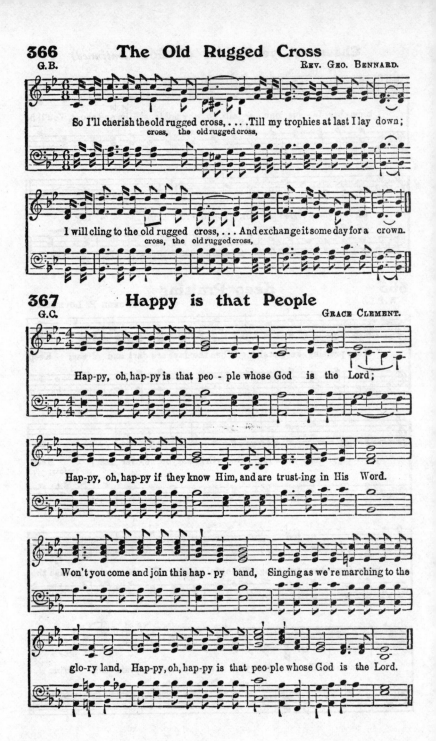

So I'll cherish the old rugged cross, ... Till my trophies at last I lay down;
cross, the old rugged cross,

I will cling to the old rugged cross, . . . And exchange it some day for a crown.
cross, the old rugged cross,

367 Happy is that People

G. C.

Grace Clement.

Hap-py, oh, hap-py is that peo - ple whose God is the Lord;

Hap-py, oh, hap-py if they know Him, and are trust-ing in His Word.

Won't you come and join this hap - py band, Singing as we're marching to the

glo-ry land, Hap-py, oh, hap-py is that peo-ple whose God is the Lord.

368

He Lives

A.H.A.

Rev. A. H. Ackley.

He lives, .. He lives, .. Christ Je-sus lives to-day! ..
He lives, He lives,

He walks with me and talks with me a-long life's nar-row way.

He lives, .. He lives, .. sal-va-tion to im-part!
He lives, He lives,

rit.

You ask me how I know He lives? He lives with-in my heart. ..

369

I fell in Love with Jesus

T.K.

Thos. Kemp.

I fell in love with Je-sus, I fell in love with Je-sus;

rall.

Wonderful day of re-joic - ing When I fell in love with my Lord.

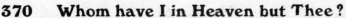

370   Whom have I in Heaven but Thee?

G.C.

GRACE CLEMENT.

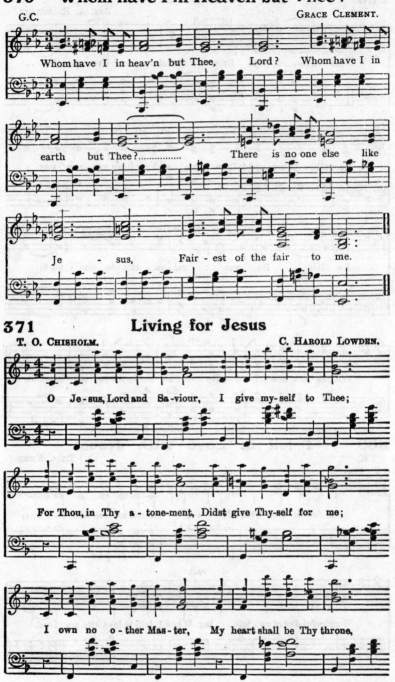

Whom have I in heav'n but Thee, Lord? Whom have I in earth but Thee?............ There is no one else like Je - sus, Fair-est of the fair to me.

371   Living for Jesus

T. O. CHISHOLM.

C. HAROLD LOWDEN.

O Je-sus, Lord and Sa-viour, I give my-self to Thee;

For Thou, in Thy a - tone-ment, Didst give Thy-self for me;

I own no o-ther Mas-ter, My heart shall be Thy throne,

Living for Jesus (continued)

My life I give, henceforth to live, O Christ, for Thee a - lone.

372 It is Blotted Out

W.R.

W. Rogers.

Vigoroso.

It is blot-ted out, yes, blot-ted out, once and for all;

My e - vil past, my black-est sin, He ne-ver will re - call.

'Tis bu - ried for e - ver in the depths of the sea;

Slower.

And now I am His, and He is mine, Halle - lu-jah, 'tis vic-to - ry!

373   We're on the Homeward Trail

Words and Music by COLONEL ARNOTT.

We're on the homeward trail,
We're on the homeward trail,
We're on the homeward trail,
We're on the homeward

Sing-ing as we go,   go - ing   home!
trail,   Sing-ing as we're go-ing, go - ing home, go-ing home!

We're on the homeward trail,
We're on the homeward trail,
We're on the homeward trail,
We're on the homeward

Sing-ing, sing-ing, sing-ing, sing-ing, go - ing   home.
trail,

By permission of the Salvation Army Music Board.

374   He gave His Life for me

IVOR POWELL.   MRS. J. POWELL

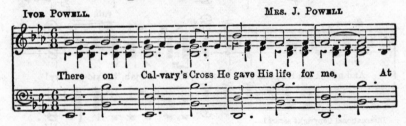

There   on   Cal-vary's Cross He gave His life   for me,   At

He gave His Life for me (continued)

such an in-finite cost, He died to set me free. I

cannot tell why He loved me, Perhaps its too much to know, I

on-ly can tell how He saved me And cleansed me as white as snow.

375 I'm going Higher some Day

H.B.

HERBERT BUFFUM.

I'm go-ing higher, yes, higher some day, I'm go-ing high-er to stay;

Over the clouds and beyond the blue sky, Going where none ever sicken or die.

Lov'd ones to meet in the 'Sweet by and by,' I'm go-ing higher some day.....
higher some day.

The Saviour's Call

Accompaniment by W. GARDNER-HUNTER.
J. JELLICOE BROWN.

J.J.B.

Je-sus is ten-der-ly call - ing, List to His voice to-

day; Earnest-ly, lov-ing-ly call - - ing,

Come to Him while you may; He took your place on

Cal - v'ry, He died to set you free; Je-sus is

'Come un - to Me.'

ten-der-ly call - ing, 'Come, sinner, come unto Me.'

'Come un - to Me.'

377 The Riven Rock my Refuge

S.S.

MR. & MRS. SETH SYKES.

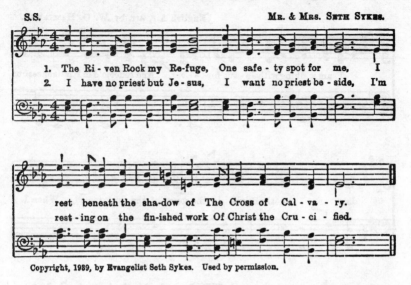

1. The Ri - ven Rock my Re-fuge, One safe - ty spot for me, I
2. I have no priest but Je - sus, I want no priest be - side, I'm

rest beneath the sha-dow of The Cross of Cal - va - ry.
rest - ing on the fin-ished work Of Christ the Cru - ci - fied.

378 There's Revival in the Air To-day

T.K.

THOS. KEMP.

There's Re - vi - val in the air to - day, . . . There's Re -
vi - val in the air to - day, There's Re - vi-val in the air, You can

bring it down with prayer, There's Re-vi - val in the air to - day.

379 I am Walking with Jesus for Ever

English Air, arr. by W. G. HATHAWAY.

I am walking with Je-sus for e-ver, And redeem'd in His likeness one day,

I shall join in the song of the ran-somed, When I get to the end of the way, . . . He will not leave me in the dawning of the morning, . . . In the splendour of the noon day He is mine, And at last in the shadows of twi-light, In the darkness His glo-ry shall shine.

His Love Won My Heart

Arranged by W. ROGERS.

Not too fast.

His love won my heart, . . A love that will nev-er de -

part; . . He took sin a-way, and came in to stay, His love

won my heart, . . . His love won my heart, . . . A

love that will nev-er de - part; . . I want to be faith-ful and

loy - al and true To the love that won my heart. . . .

381   We'll Sing in the Morning

T. Llewellyn Barry.

We'll sing in the morning the songs of sal-va-tion, We'll

sing in the noontide the songs of His love; And

when we ar-rive at the end of the jour-ney, We'll

sing the songs of Zi-on in the courts a-bove.

Repeat (ad. lib.) an octave higher with right hand throughout.
(Words by permission of the Salvation Army Board.)
May also be sung to the tune "Bells of St. Mary's."

382   A Song of the Mercies of God

Arrangement by W. G. Hathaway.

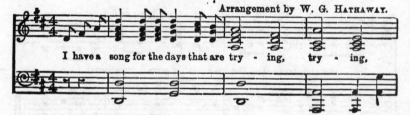

I have a song for the days that are try-ing, try-ing,

A Song of the Mercies of God (*continued*)

try - ing, I have a song for the days that are try - ing, A song of the mercies of God. Great is His love and com-pas - sion, He is a Re-fuge, A Strength in time of need, I have a song for the days that are try - ing, A song of the mercies of God.

By permission of the Salvation Army Music Board.

383   Lord, I Believe

Lord, I believe, Lord, I believe! Saviour, raise my faith in Thee, Till it can move a mountain; Lord, I believe, Lord, I believe! All my doubts are buried in the fountain.

Trav'lling with my Saviour

R. E. DARRAGH

A. W. EDSOR.

Trav'lling with my Sa - viour, through the e-ne-my's land,

Trav'lling with my Sa - viour, walk-ing hand in hand,

He is e-ver with me, I need ne-ver fear,

Trav'lling with my Sa-viour, with my Lord down here,

Trav'lling with my Sa-viour, with my Lord down here.

385   That's why I Love Him

S.L. Arr.

SCOTT LAWRENCE

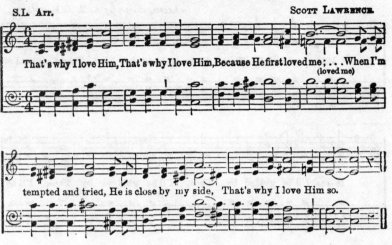

That's why I love Him, That's why I love Him, Because He first loved me; ... When I'm
(loved me)

tempted and tried, He is close by my side, That's why I love Him so.

386   I know the Lord will make a Way

I know the Lord will make a way   for me, ... I know the

Lord will make a way for   me; ...   If I live a ho-ly life, Shun the

wrong and do the right, I know the Lord will make a way for me. .....

I'll be Guided by Thee

Arrangement by A. E. A. HAYWARD.

I'll be guid-ed by Thee, I'll be guid-ed by Thee; Thou Shepherd of Is-rael I'll be guided by Thee, I'll be guid-ed by Thee, I'll be guid-ed by Thee; Thou Shepherd of Is - rael I'll be guid-ed by Thee.

Walking with Jesus

ANON.

Arr. by W. G. HATHAWAY.

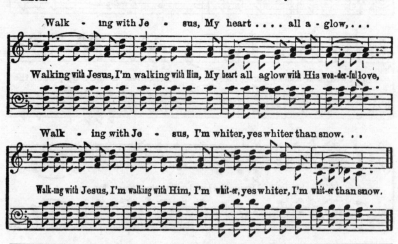

Walk - ing with Je - sus, My heart .... all a - glow, ...
Walking with Jesus, I'm walking with Him, My heart all aglow with His won-der-ful love,

Walk - ing with Je - sus, I'm whiter, yes whiter than snow. . .
Walk-ing with Jesus, I'm walking with Him, I'm whit-er, yes whiter, I'm whit-er than snow.

Elim Publishing Co. Ltd., Clapham Crescent. London, S.W.4. —16964

Elim Choruses No. 8

389

W.G.H.

Sing as you Go

W. Gardner-Hunter.

Allegro.

Sing as you go, keep sing-ing, Ne-ver let your faith in God grow dim; Sing as you go, keep sing-ing, Always firmly put your trust in Him; Sing as you go, keep sing-ing, To the world your Christian courage shew; Tho' the way be dark, rejoice, Praise the Lord with heart and voice, Sing as you go, sing as you go, sing as you go.

390 **Through to the Throne**

E. C. W. Boulton.

C. C. Swift.

Through to the throne, Lord, shew me the way;
oh, shew me the way;
In-to Thy vic-t'ry lift me, I pray.
In-to Thy vic-to-ry lift me, oh, lift me, I pray.
Reigning with Thee, Lord, shar-ing Thy pow'r, . . .
yes, shar-ing Thy power,
Love's rich en-due-ment, mine ev-'ry hour.

391 **He is able to make me stand**

G.C.

Grace Clement.

He is a-ble to make me stand, He will hold me by His
hand, He will keep my feet on the King's high-way Till I

reach the land of per-fect day, He is a-ble, He is

a- - ble, He is a - ble to make me stand.

392   The 'K.L.U.' Chorus

ANNABELLA G. REID.   W. GARDNER-HUNTER.

Keep look-ing up for Je-sus, He's coming back some day,— He

came to earth to save us, Then to Heav'n He went a-way; Some

glad day we will meet Him, When He comes to claim His own— *Keep

look-ing up for Je-sus, And you'll ne-ver, ne-ver feel a-lone.

*(Or ' So K.L.U. for Jesus.')

393

Christ the Lord is Risen!

A.P.G.

ALFRED P. GIBBS. Har. by CLIFFORD LLOYDE.

Christ the Lord is ri - sen! Vic - to - ry is won! All the work that saves the sin - ner has been done! Now through faith in Him, God of - fers full and free, Pardon, peace and joy and glorious li - ber - ty!

394

Christ's Ambassadors

MRS. G. W.

MRS. GEO. WAGNER.

We are Christ's am - bas - sa - dors; And our colours we must un - furl,

we're marching,

We must wear a spotless robe, Clean and righteous be-fore the world.

we're walking,

We must show we're cleans'd from sin; And that Je - sus dwells with - in,

oh, glory

Proving du-ly that we're tru-ly Christ's am-bas-sa - dors. (ambas-sa-dors.)

395 ## L - O - V - E

F. D. B.

Melody by F. D. Byatt.
Arranged by A. E. A. Hayward.

L - O - V - E, That spells love;

Love brought Je - sus from a - bove,

Made Him suf - fer on the tree,—

Oh, 'twas love for you and me.

396

Shelter Me

G.C.

GRACE CLEMENT.

Shel - ter me, shel - ter me, Close to Thy lov - ing breast;

Shel - ter me, shel - ter me, There let me lie and rest,

Till the sha - dows take their flight, And the dark - ness turns to

light, Shel - ter me, Lord Je - sus, shel - ter me.

397

Sunshine in the Heart

F.D M.

Allegretto.

F. D. MORRISON.

Give me sunshine in my heart all a - long life's way, For 'tis sunshine in the

heart makes the bright - est day; If Je - sus is with me, Then

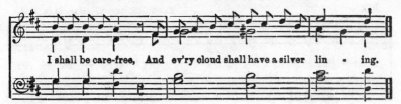

I shall be care-free, And ev'ry cloud shall have a silver lin - ing.

398 **I Need a Hand to Guide Me**

E. M.

MRS. E. MAYSON.

Arrangement by A. E. A. HAYWARD.

I need a hand to guide me, As I walk the narrow way; . . For the
path is steep and thorny, And oft I go a-stray, But a
lov - ing hand is guid-ing me, That I no more should roam; 'Tis the
pierc-ed hand of Je - sus That leads me right home.

399 **His Love is the Joy of My Heart**

P.H.

PAUL HUTCHINS. Har. MRS. P.H.

His love is the joy of my heart, His love is the joy of my

heart to-day: And all of the time, the Saviour is mine: From Him I will

ne - ver de - part, . . . His love is the joy of my heart, His

will ne-ver de-part,

love is the joy of my heart to - day; I'm hap-py and free, He

ad lib.

sa - tis - fies me: His love is the joy, the joy of my heart.

400 **I Belong to the King**

IDA D. REED.

MAURICE A. CLIFTON.

I be - long to the King, I'm a child of His love, And He

I belong to the King (continued)

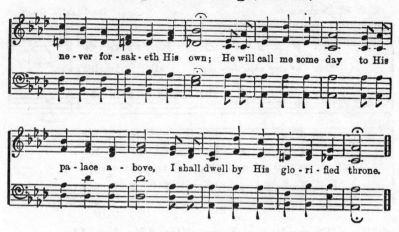

ne-ver for-sak-eth His own; He will call me some day to His

pa-lace a-bove, I shall dwell by His glo-ri-fied throne.

401 I will Go Hand in Hand with Jesus

W. W. KIRKBY.

MRS. DORIS HUDSON.

I will go hand in hand with Je-sus, Trusting Him whate'er be-

fall; Where He leads I'll fol-low, For He's my all in all.

Not a doubt, not a care, or wor-ry, Shall here my path-way

mar; With Je-sus, Halle-lu-jah! As my ev-er guiding star.

402 Temples of the Spirit

E. C. W. Boulton.

Douglas B. Gray.

Step by step with Je - sus, All a-long life's way, . .

Now the cross and con - flict, Then the per-fect day.

403 There's no Love like His for Me

John L. Newkirk.

Powell G. Fithian.

There ne - ver was one like Je - - sus, Ev - er,

al - ways true is He; There ne - ver was one like

Je - - sus, There's no love like His love for me. . . .

404 Feasting with my Lord

John S. Brown.

L. O. Brown.

Feasting, I am feast-ing, Feast-ing with my Lord; I'm

feast-ing, I am feast-ing On the liv-ing Word.

405 When Ye See These Things

L.W.   Air by Miss L. Walker, Har. by A. E. A. Hayward.

When ye see these things come to pass,   When ye see these things come to

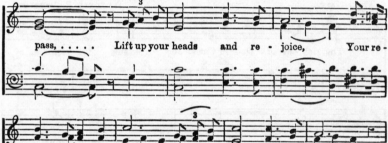

pass, ... Lift up your heads and re - joice, Your re-

demp-tion draweth nigh. Lift up your heads and re - joice,

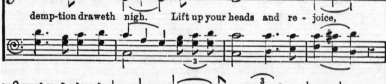

Praise the Lord with heart and voice, ... Lift up your heads and re-

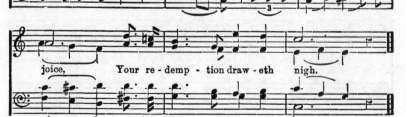

joice, Your re - demp - tion draw - eth nigh.

406 Jesus, Let Thy Splendour

E. C. W. BOULTON.

MARJORIE HELYER.

Fel - lowship with Je - sus, This is vic - to - ry,

They who own His lordship Know true li - ber - ty.

407 The Riches of God

FRED NAPP.

WENDELL P. LOVELESS.

The rich - es of God in Christ Je - - sus, The rich - es of

God in Him; . . . . With His glo - ry di - vine, All

His shall be mine, The rich - es of God in Him. . . .

408 Christ is Not a Disappointment

C. W. WAGGONER.

C. HAROLD LOWDEN.

Christ is not a dis - ap-point-ment, Ev-'ry long-ing in my breast,

Finds in Him complete ful-fil-ment, He has brought me in-to rest.

I have test-ed Him and prov'd Him More than all I dream'd He'd be;

Christ is not a dis-ap-pointment, He is all in all to me.

409 On that Bright and Golden Morning

F. J. CROSBY.   IRA D. SANKEY.

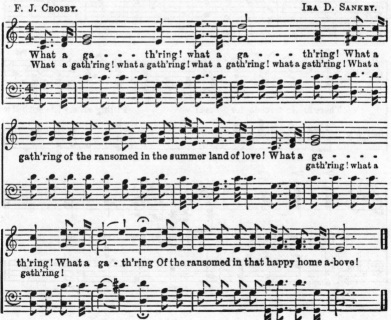

What a ga - - - th'ring! what a ga - - - th'ring! What a
What a gath'ring! what a gath'ring! what a gath'ring! what a gath'ring! What a

gath'ring of the ransomed in the summer land of love! What a ga - - - -
                                                          gath'ring! what a

th'ring! What a ga - th'ring Of the ransomed in that happy home a-bove!
gath'ring!

Jesus is My Precious Saviour

Kenneth H. Banks.
Moderato. *mf*

Kenneth H. Banks.

Je-sus is my pre-cious Sa - viour, He is all in all to me; For He shed His blood on Cal - v'ry, From my sin to set me free; He it is Who lives in glo - ry, There to in-tercede for me; Filling all my life with His joy and peace, And my soul with ecs - ta - cy.

411 Jesus, Lead Me up the Mountain

Anon.

C. F. Weigele.

Bring me high - - - - er up the moun - tain, In - to
Bring me high - er up the moun - tain,

fel - - - lowship with Thee, In Thy light . . I see the
In - to fellowship, sweet fellowship with Thee; In Thy light I see the

foun - tain, And the blood that cleanseth me.
that cleanseth me.

412 I Bel'eve God Answers Prayer

Bessie Porter Head.

Rev. Harold Green.

I be - lieve God an - swers pray'r, I am sure God an - swers

pray'r, I have proved God an - swers pray'r, Glo - ry to His Name.

Published by permission of the South Africa General Mission.

"Whosoever!" That Means Me

A.E A.H.

A. E. A. HAYWARD.

Who-so-e-ver drink-eth the wa-ter I shall give, He shall ne-ver

Bass in 8ves.

thirst a - gain...... Yea! those 'who-so - e - vers' e -

ter - nal life shall have, who call up-on the Sa-viour's name.

Oh, that bless-ed 'who - so - e • • ver' Leaves no doubt as

I can see...... Oh, praise His ho-ly name, His word

makes it all so plain. 'Who - so - e-ver!' that means ME! ....

414 Beautiful Dawn

F.M.J.

FRANCES M. JOHNSTON.

There's a beau-ti-ful dawn a-wait ing, Radiant with Heav'n's own light, . .

Alto prominent.

When the Saviour His loved ones will ga - ther
Heav'n's own light,

Out of the shades of night. There's a beau-ti-ful dawn a-
dawn a-wait-ing;

wait - ing; God's love will all a - dorn, . . Oh, what joy will be
adorn.

there in that homeland so fair; *ad lib.* Oh, what a beau-ti-ful morn!

415

If you Believe and I Believe

Anon.

Arrangement by A. E. A. HAYWARD

If you be-lieve and I believe and we to-ge-ther strive;

The Ho - ly Spi - rit will come down and *--- will re - vive,

and *--- will re - vive, and *--- will re - vive,

The Ho - ly spi - rit will come down And *--- will re - vive.

The name of any town or district may be sung.

416

Praise Him with Melody

MATHILDA LONG.

CLINTON D. LOWDEN.

Praise Him with me-lo-dy, Praise Him with song, Tell of His

ho-li-ness All the day long; Give Him all ma-jes-ty Earth can af -

Praise Him with Melody—*continued*

ford, Praise Him with me - lo - dy, Praise ye the Lord.

417

Joy of Heaven

G. D. BETHANY.   W. GARDNER-HUNTER.

Heaven fills my soul since Christ took con-trol— In my heart He

lives, Wondrous joy, He gives; Love-light gilds the way To e-

ter - nal day, 'Joy of Hea-ven' fills my soul.

418 When I Think of His Love for Me

E. E. HEWITT.

B. D. ACKLEY.

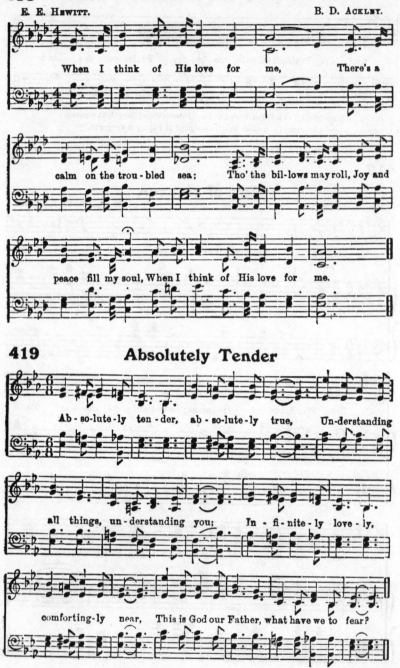

When I think of His love for me, There's a calm on the trou-bled sea; Tho' the bil-lows may roll, Joy and peace fill my soul, When I think of His love for me.

419 Absolutely Tender

Ab - so - lute - ly ten - der, ab - so - lute - ly true, Un-derstanding all things, un-derstanding you; In - fi - nite - ly love - ly, comforting-ly near, This is God our Father, what have we to fear?

420 It is Morning in My Heart

A.H.A.

REV. A. H. ACKLEY.

It is morning, it is morning in my heart, . . .
in my heart,
Jesus made the gloomy shadows all de-part; . . .
made all de-part;
Songs of gladness now I sing, for since Je-sus is my King, It is morning, it is morning in my heart.

421 Hallelujah for the Cleansing Blood

Arrangement by A. E. A. HAYWARD.

Hal-le-lu-jah for the cleans-ing blood, Hal-le-lu-jah for the heal-ing blood, Hal-le-lu-jah for the pre-cious blood: Vic-to-rious blood of Je-sus.

422   **A Melody in My Heart**

S. E. C.   SIDNEY E. COX.

In my heart   to-day, There's a mel-o-dy in my heart to-day,   I

In my heart   to-day,   to-day,

carried a heavy burden But it rolled away; There's a melo-dy in my heart to-day.

423   **Steal away Alone with Jesus**

W. G. H.   Arranged by W. G. HATHAWAY.

Slowly, with feeling.

Steal a-way a - lone with Je - - sus, Steal a-way a -

lone with Him. . . . When you kneel with Him in pray'r, He makes the

rit.

bur-den light to bear, If you on - ly steal a-way a-lone with Him.

Tramp along the Highway

Slow march.

A. E. A. HAYWARD.

Tramp, tramp, tramp along the high-way like the three wise men of old, . . . Came and worship'd, then present-ed gifts, Not on-ly of myrrh, but frankincense and gold His star led them, but His ban-ner o'er us leads us onward whilst we sing this chorus, Tramp, tramp tramp along the King's own high-way, Leading upward to God.

425

Charmed by the Cross

D.B.G.

D. B. GRAY.

Charmed by the Cross, . . . en-rap-tured with it's sto - ry,

'Twas there my Sa - viour bore a - way my sin . . . . . .

Dark - ness with - in . . . . . was chang'd to Hea - ven's Glo - ry,

Till He doth come, His prais - es will I sing. . . .

426

Just One Day Nearer Home

W. G. H.

Arranged by W. G. HATHAWAY.

Just one day nearer home, The shadows of the night de - scend; Just

one day less to roam, While ev'ning twilight colours blend. Be -

neath the star-ry dome I rest be-side my Guide and Friend.

Each day tramping, night-ly camping, One day near-er home.

427 Longing for the Morning

H.A.C.

Vivaciously.

H. A. COURT.

I am longing for the morn-ing, I am longing for my Lord to come;

Longing for the night of sin to pass, Longing to reach my home.

'Come quickly,' saith my soul, O Sa-viour I would see Thy face,

Then thro' the ages shall my glad song roll—I'm a sin-ner saved by grace.

428 Old Things are Passed away

Mrs. C.H.M.

Mrs. C. H. Morris.

Old things are passed a - way, . . . old things are passed a - way, . . .
Old things are passed a - way, old things are passed a - way,

All things in Christ have new become Since Je - sus came to stay; . . .

How won - der-ful the change with-in my heart and life to - day, . . .

All things in Christ have new be-come, Old things are passed a - way.

429 Keep Me in the Shadow of the Cross

Fred. A. Brock, Jnr.
Slowly.

Paul Hutchens,
Har. by Mrs. P. H.

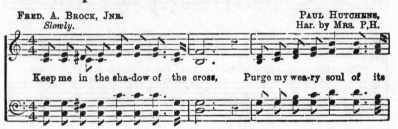

Keep me in the sha-dow of the cross, Purge my wea-ry soul of its

430 ### Don't Turn Him Away

Arranged by A. E. A. HAYWARD.

dross,   Fill me with Thy spi - rit till the whole wide world may see

The Light that shone from Cal - va - ry,   Shining out through me.

Don't turn Him a - way, a - way;   Don't turn Him a - way (a - way);

He will come back to your heart again, Altho' you have gone a - stray;

a - stray, a - stray;

e - ter - nal day?

Who will you have to plead your cause   On that e-ter - nal, e - ternal day?

Don't turn the Saviour away from your heart, Don't turn Him a - way. . .

431 Come, Holy Spirit

W. R. McKibbin.
Prayerfully.

A. Rowley.

Come, Ho-ly Spi-rit, Right in-to my soul;

Come in Thy full-ness, Take now full con-trol.

Fill with Thy power This tem-ple of clay,

While I am wait-ing, Bap-tise me to-day.

432 Love Led Him to Calvary

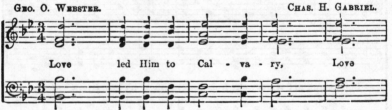

Geo. O. Webster.

Chas. H. Gabriel.

Love led Him to Cal-va-ry, Love

Love led Him to Calvary—*continued*

led Him to Cal - va - ry; Seek-ing the lost, at the

ut - ter-most cost, Love led Him to Cal - va - ry.

433   I am the Resurrection

NORMAN J. CLAYTON.

I am the re - surrec-tion and the life,
I am the re - sur - rection and the life,
He that be -

lieveth in me tho' He were dead,
lieveth in me though He were dead,
Yet shall He live,

Yet shall He live, And who - so - e - ver liv - eth and be -

liev - eth in me shall ne - ver, ne - ver die.
ne - ver, ne - ver.

434   I'm on the Victory Side

E.R.F.   ELDEN R. FARRAR.

1. Oh, I'm liv-ing on the vic-t'ry side, I'm liv-ing on the
2. Oh, come o-ver on the vic-t'ry side, Come o-ver on the
3. Are you liv-ing on the vic-t'ry side? Are you liv-ing on the

vic-t'ry side, . . There is vic-t'ry, grace and pow'r In each
vic-t'ry side, . . There is vic-t'ry, grace and pow'r In each
vic-t'ry side? . . There is vic-t'ry, grace and pow'r In each

try-ing hour, I'm liv-ing on the vic-t'ry side.
try-ing hour, Come o-ver on the vic-t'ry side.
try-ing hour, Are you liv-ing on the vic-t'ry side?

435   In the Garden

C.A.M.   C. AUSTIN MILES.

And He walks with me, and He talks with me, And He tells me I am his own,

And the joy we share as we tar-ry there, None o-ther has e-ver known.

Remembered No More

E. MARGARET CLARKSON.

B. D. ACKLEY.

Re-membered, re-membered no more, ... My sins are re

re - membered no more,

membered no more; . . . They are lost in the depths of His

re - membered no more;

fathomless love, And re-membered, re-membered no more. . . .

re - membered no more.

437 How greatly Jesus must have loved me

J. W. Y.

REV. J. W. YOUNG.

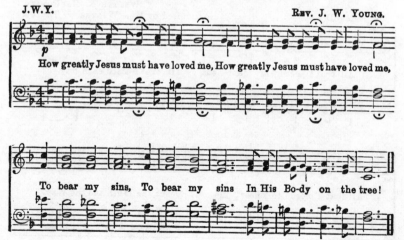

How greatly Jesus must have loved me, How greatly Jesus must have loved me,

To bear my sins, To bear my sins In His Bo-dy on the tree!

With One Accord

E. May Grimes.

H. Green.

Pour down Thy Spi - rit once a-gain, dear Lord; Our cry goes

up to Thee for 'lat - ter rain'; U - nite Thy peo - ple

as the 'heart of one,' And Pente - costal days shall come a - gain!

All that I Need is Jesus

Walter R. MacDonald,
Harmonised by Mrs. Walter G. Taylor.

W. R. MacD.

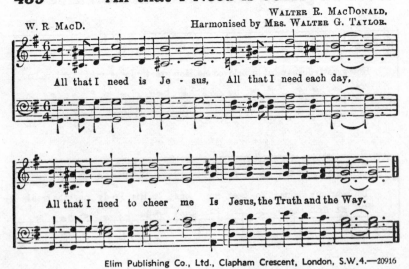

All that I need is Je - sus, All that I need each day,

All that I need to cheer me Is Jesus, the Truth and the Way.

Elim Publishing Co., Ltd., Clapham Crescent, London, S.W.4.—20916

Elim Choruses, No. 9

440   Lord of my Life

P. E. RONAN.

Won-der-ful, won-der-ful, won-der-ful love, Love which brought Jesus from hea-ven a - bove; Down from the heights to the depths Je - sus came, Lift-ing me up to the heights, praise His name. Won-der-ful, won-der-ful, won-der-ful love, Love which brought Je-sus from hea -ven a - bove, Lord of my life I shall own .. Him, For such wonderful, wonderful love.

Who-so-e-ver will to the Lord may come, Who-so-e-ver will to the

Lord may come, Who-so-e-ver will to the Lord may come He'll not turn one a-

way. Je-sus, Je-sus, heals the broken-hearted,
Je-sus, Je-sus,

Je-sus, Je-sus, heals the broken-hearted, Je-sus,
Je-sus, Je-sus, Jesus,

Je-sus, (Jesus.) heals the broken-hearted, He will set you free.

442 Fill Me Now

E. H. STOKES, D.D.

JNO. R. SWEENEY.

Fill me now, fill me now, Je-sus, come and fill me now!

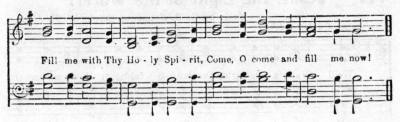

Fill me with Thy Ho - ly Spi - rit, Come, O come and fill me now!

443   Say, will You be Ready?

Anon.

Arrangement by A. E. A. HAYWARD.

Say, will you be rea - dy when Je - sus comes?

Are you sure you're born a - gain and washed in Je - su's blood? . .

Are your garments spot-less? . . Are they white as snow? Say, will

you be rea - dy when Je - sus comes?

444   Jesus, the Light of the World!

Music by G. D. ELDERKIN, arr. by W. H. JUDE.

We'll walk in the light, the beau-ti-ful light; Oh, come where the
dew-drops of mer-cy are bright! Shine all a-round us by
day and by night: Je-sus, the Light of the world!

445   I have Seen the Face of Jesus

FRANCES BEVAN, W. P. L.

WENDELL P. LOVELESS.

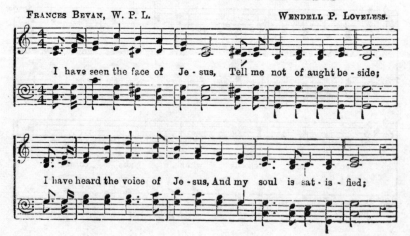

I have seen the face of Je-sus, Tell me not of aught be-side;
I have heard the voice of Je-sus, And my soul is sat-is-fied;

I have Seen the Face of Jesus—*continued*.

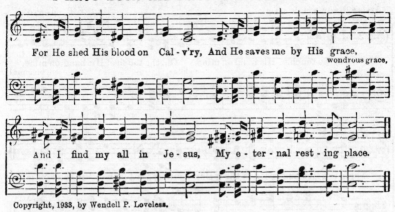

For He shed His blood on Cal - v'ry, And He saves me by His grace,
wondrous grace,

And I find my all in Je - sus, My e - ter - nal rest - ing place.

446 When My Feet Press Pavements Golden

Rev. T. C. Henderson.   Mrs. T. C. Henderson.

When my feet press pavements golden there be - side the cry - stal sea,

I shall know faith's con - sum - ma - tion and my blest Re - deem - er see;

With im - mor - tals of all a - ges I shall know as I am known,

And go out no more for - e - ver from the ra - diance of His throne.

447   The Touch of His Hand on Mine

JESSIE BROWN POUNDS.   HENRY P. MORTON.

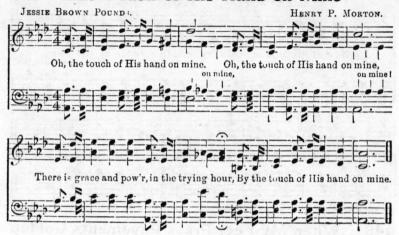

Oh, the touch of His hand on mine, Oh, the touch of His hand on mine, on mine, on mine!

There is grace and pow'r, in the trying hour, By the touch of His hand on mine.

448   Break every Fetter for Me

Words and Music by SETH SYKES.   Harmonised by Mrs. SETH SYKES.

Break ev'ry fetter for me, dear Lord, Break ev'ry fet-ter for me,

Give me the vict'ry o'er ev-'ry sin, Take full possesion, cleanse me within,

Break ev'ry fet-ter for me, dear Lord, break ev-'ry fet-ter for me.

449 Far, Far on the other Side

PAUL RADER.

ARTHUR W. McKEE.

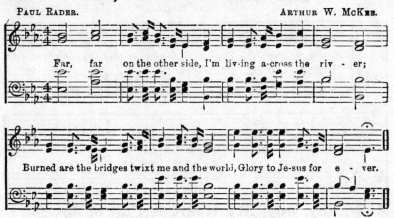

Far, far on the other side, I'm living a-cross the riv - er;

Burned are the bridges twixt me and the world, Glory to Je-sus for e - ver.

450 The Heart that was Broken for Me

J. W. VAN DE VENTER.

They crown'd Him with thorns. He was beaten with stripes; He was smitten and
I'll take up my cross, I will walk by His side, For the pathway of

nailed to the tree, (to the tree,) But the pain in His heart was the
du - ty I see, (yes, I see,) I will fol - low my Lord and a -

rit.

hard-est to bear, The heart that was broken for me. (for me.)
bide in His heart, The heart that was broken for me. (for me.)

451 Jesus, Fill me with Thy Spirit

D.H.   MRS. D. HUDSON, arr. by E. P. GRAHAME.

Je - sus, fill me with Thy Spi - it; Cleanse me with Thy pow'r di-vine;

Fill me, use me pre-cious Saviour, Till my will is lost in Thine.

452 Joy, Joy, My Heart is Full of Joy

Arr. by W. G. HATHAWAY.

Joy, joy, my heart is full of joy; Joy, joy, my heart is full of joy. My

Saviour dear is ever near, That's the reason why my heart is full of joy.

This Chorus may be sung as a Roundelay. One section of the congregation begins first, and when they reach *, the other section joins in at the beginning of the Air.

453 Think on Me

Words adapted by JACQUES HOPKINS.   Melody by LADY JOHN SCOTT.

1. When wea - ry sigh-ing For pleasures fly-ing, When hope is dy - ing,
2. Thy bo - dy bro - ken, Thy cross the to - ken, God's love hath spo - ken,
3. When foes are by us, When woes are nigh us, When friends decry us,

Think on Me—*continued*.

Grant us grace, O Lord, . . . to think on Thee, think on Thee.

454 His Banner over Me is Love

Arr. by W. G. HATHAWAY.

His ban-ner o-ver me is love, His ban-ner o-ver me is

love; He brought me in-to His banqueting house, And His banner o-ver

me is love, is love, is love, His
His ban-ner o-ver me, His ban-ner o-ver me,
is love,

ban-ner o-ver me is love; He brought me in-to His

ban-quet-ing house, And His ban-ner o-ver me is love.

455 ## Whisper a Prayer

Arr. by W. G. HATHAWAY.

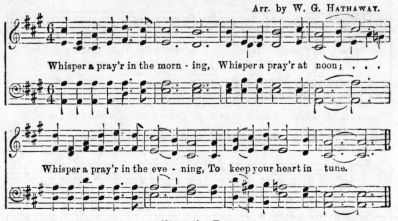

Whisper a pray'r in the morn - ing, Whisper a pray'r at noon; . . .

Whisper a pray'r in the eve - ning, To keep your heart in tune.

Alternative Verses.

God answers prayer in the morning,
  God answers prayer at noon;
God answers prayer in the evening,
  So keep your heart in tune.

Jesus may come in the morning,
  Jesus may come at noon;
Jesus may come in the evening,
  So keep your heart in tune.

456 ## Come and Confirm Thy Word

Brightly.

T. WOODS.

Come and confirm Thy Word, Come and confirm Thy Word; Let signs and

wonders be done in Thy Name, Spread far and wide Thy glo-ry and fame;

Sinners, O Lord, for Thee we will claim, So come and confirm Thy Word.

C.S.

CONSTANCE SMITH.

I met Je-sus at the cross roads, Where the two ways meet;

Satan too was standing there, And he said, 'Come this way, Lots and lots of

pleasures I can give to you to-day.' But I said, 'No, there's Je-sus here, Just

see what He of-fers me: Down here my sins for-giv-en, Up

there, a home in heaven; ' Praise God! that's the way for me.

He'll Carry Your Burden

CONSTANCE SMITH.

He'll car - ry your burden and lighten your load, If you'll on - ly come to Him

now. . . . My Saviour is will-ing your sins to for-give, Just

come at His feet lowly bow; . . . He died on the cross full sal -

vation to give, He died that you might be free; . . He'll carry your

burden and lighten your load, If you'll on - ly come to Him now.

459   **Jesus, Jesus is our Song**

Je - sus, Je - sus, is our song to-day; Je - sus, Je - sus,

all along the way; He will guide us e - ver, He will fail us ne - ver,

Till we reach our happy home a-bove. Je - sus, Je - sus,

blessed Friend divine; Je - sus, Je - sus, how His light doth shine: We will

shout and sing His wondrous love, While marching 'neath His banner glo- rious.

460 Wonderful Peace

W. D. Cornell. Altd.   W. G. Cooper.

Peace! peace! wonderful peace, Coming down from the Father a-bove; Sweep

o - ver my spirit for - e-ver, I pray, In fathomless billows of love.

My Life is Thine

A. D. H.

A. D. Hathaway.

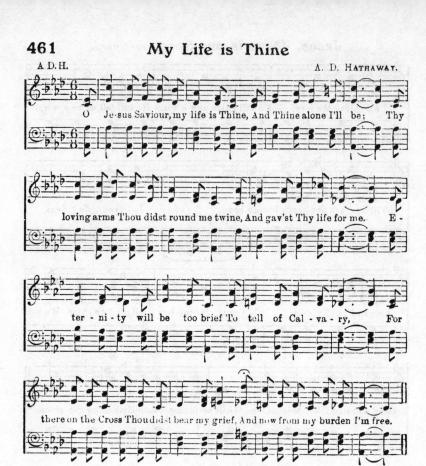

O Je-sus Saviour, my life is Thine, And Thine alone I'll be; Thy
loving arms Thou didst round me twine, And gav'st Thy life for me. E-
ter - ni - ty will be too brief To tell of Cal - va - ry, For
there on the Cross Thou didst bear my grief, And now from my burden I'm free.

462

Jesus took my Burden

Rev. Johnston Oatman, Jnr.

Bertha Mae Lillenas.

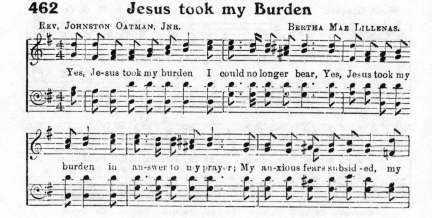

Yes, Je-sus took my burden I could no longer bear, Yes, Jesus took my
burden in an-swer to my prayer; My an-xious fears subsid-ed, my

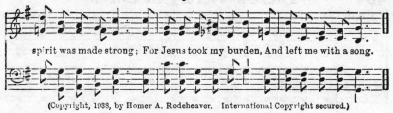

spirit was made strong; For Jesus took my burden, And left me with a song.

463 Saved at Last

W. J. PATTERSON. Air by E. STEVENS, arr. E. STEVENS, Jnr.

Saved at last, and the work is done;

Safe and blest, vic-to-ry won.

Jor-dan passed, from sin set free.

Hal-le-lu-jah! Jesus, my Saviour now lives in me.

464   There's Victory in Christ

A.D.H.

A. D. HATHAWAY.

There's vic-to-ry in Christ, Yes, vic-to-ry for me; There's vic-to-ry in Christ, For He has set me free. His blood doth now a-tone, And I am His a-lone: There's pow'r to o-ver-come, There's vic-to-ry.

465   I Know He Loves and Cares

F. SPENCER JOHNSON.
Adapted from Capt. G. W. Dawkin's air.

F.S.J.

Gradually slower.

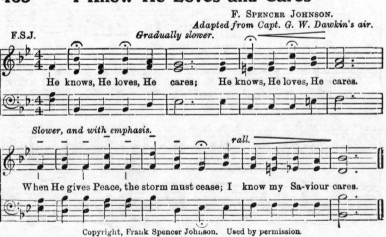

He knows, He loves, He cares; He knows, He loves, He cares.

Slower, and with emphasis.

rall.

When He gives Peace, the storm must cease; I know my Sa-viour cares.

466

Someday

T.K.

EVANGELIST THOMAS KEMP.

Some — day I'll look up-on Je - sus, Some — day I'll gaze on His face: Caught up with clouds in - to glo - ry, Saved by His won-der-ful grace. . .

(Used by permission. Happy Heart Gospel Press, Liverpool, 14.)

467 He stooped, and smiled, then lifted me

D. KEENAN.

D. J. THOMAS.

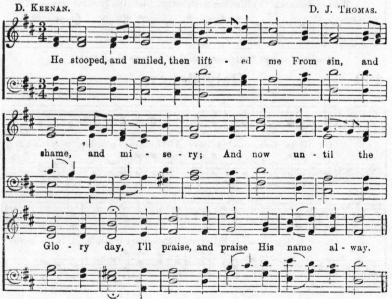

He stooped, and smiled, then lift - ed me From sin, and shame, 'and mi - se-ry; And now un - til the Glo - ry day, I'll praise, and praise His name al - way.

468 Thanksgiving Chorus

Psalm ciii.

Fred H. Squire.

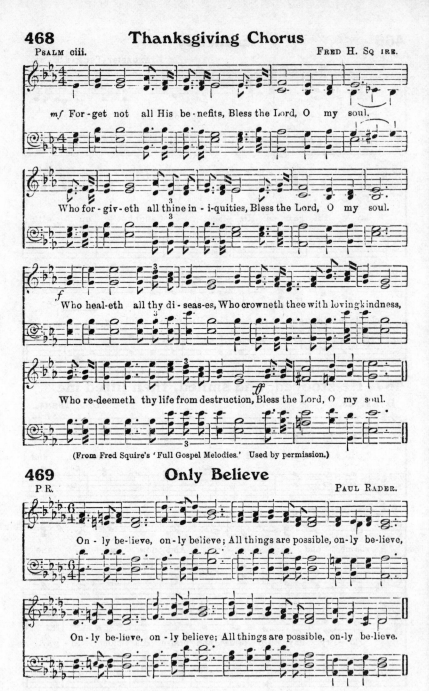

mf For-get not all His be-nefits, Bless the Lord, O my soul.

Who for-giv-eth all thine in - i-quities, Bless the Lord, O my soul.

f Who heal-eth all thy di - seas-es, Who crowneth thee with lovingkindness,

Who re-deemeth thy life from destruction, Bless the Lord, O my soul.

(From Fred Squire's 'Full Gospel Melodies.' Used by permission.)

469 Only Believe

P R.

Paul Rader.

On - ly be-lieve, on - ly believe; All things are possible, on-ly be-lieve,

On - ly be-lieve, on - ly believe; All things are possible, on-ly be-lieve.

Crown the Saviour

M.D.

MERRILL DUNLOP.

O why not crown the Sa - viour King of your heart, King of your
heart, and ne'er - fail-ing Friend? O why not crown the Sa - viour
King of your heart, Why not crown Him to - day?

471

Every Day with Him

J. E. RUECKERT.

CORNELIUS C. KEUR, JR.

Ev'ry day is sweeter when I walk with Him, Ev'ry day is brighter when I
talk with Him; His presence e-ver cheers me; I know He's al - ways
near me, In my heart's ' The blessed Hope,' I look for Him.

Wondrous Melody

Words and Music by Fred. H. Squire.

1. Won - drous me - lo - dy, Ring - ing in my heart to -
2. Won - drous lib - er - ty, Je-su's love has set me

1st time.

- day, ... Fill - ing me, Thrill - ing me, And
free; .... light - ing up my way. ....

2nd time.

O what bliss di-vine,

Just to know He's mine, And to know that Jesus cares for me! ....

(From Fred. Squire's 'Full Gospel Melodies.' Used by permission.)

473 Altogether Lovely

H. A. Ironside. Florence E. Dahlstrom.

He is al - to-ge-ther love-ly, Yes, the fair - est of the fair,

Chief is He a-mong ten thousand, And with Him I'll glo-ry share.

474 **J is for the Joy**

Words and Air by Mrs. D. Walters.   Arrangement by S. Long.

J is for the joy which Je-sus gives me; E is for His e-verlasting love; S is for the sweetness of His pre-sence; U is for His unction from a - bove; S is for salvation which He gave me In His dy-ing love on Calva - ry. Put them al-to-gether they spell Je-sus, The sweetest Name on earth to me.

8ve.

8ve.

(From Fred Squire's ' Full Gospel Melodies.' Used by permission.)

475
G.B.

The Road Leads Home

Rev. George Bennard.

Yes, the road leads home, Yes, the road leads home; It is
(the road leads   the road leads home;)

of-ten rough and thorn-y, But the road leads home; And my

Saviour's gone be-fore me, He has giv'n His word to cheer me, So I'm

sing-ing as I jour-ney, For the road leads home.

476

Deep and Wide

Deep and wide, deep and wide, There's a fountain flowing deep and wide.

Deep and wide, deep and wide, There's a fountain flowing deep and wide.

O what a Wonderful Promise!

A.E.A.H.

A. E. A. Hayward.

Oh! what a won-der-ful pro-mise He gave, That who-so-e'er will be-lieve.... On Je-sus Christ and His pow-er to save, E-ter-nal life shall re-ceive.... Rest for the wea-ry, His peace will en-thrall, A home in Hea-ven, to you He doth call; Don't let your way-wardness rob you of all, Don't let Old Sa-tan de-ceive.

A.E.A.H. *Slow march.*

A. E. A. HAYWARD.

Tramping a - long on the up - ward way, Eyes fixed on Je - sus, the Light of day; In - to the night shadows, come what may, A saved, and a deathless ar - my. Fear - ing no ob - sta - cle through the night, Trusting the Saviour, who leads the fight; Thro' death's dark vale to mansions bright, A glo-rious e - ter - nal ar - my.

479 Help Me to be Like Him

A. Neilson.
Slowly and prayerfully.

MRS. A. NEILSON.

Help me to be like Him, Help me to be like Him,

Loving and kind and for-bear-ing, Com-fort-ing, lift-ing and

cheering. Help me to be like Him, Help me to be

like Him, Meek, gen-tle, for-giv-ing, A life of

vic-to-ry liv-ing,— Help me to be like Him.

A.P.G.

Reverently.

ALFRED P. GIBBS.

'Chief - est of ten thou - sand,' Fair - est of the fair,

'Al - to-gether love - ly,' Be-yond all com - pare!

Lord of all cre - a - tion, Man of Cal - va - ry,

'Son of God Who loved And gave Himself for me!'

481 Thou wilt Keep Him in Perfect Peace

V. A. K.

VIVIAN A. KRETZ.

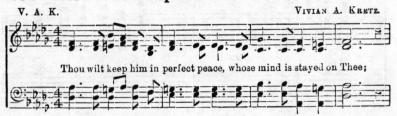

Thou wilt keep him in perfect peace, whose mind is stayed on Thee;

Thou wilt Keep Him in Perfect Peace—*continued.*

When the shadows come and darkness falls, He giveth inward peace; Oh, He

is the on-ly perfect rest-ing place, He giv-eth per-fect peace;

Thou wilt keep him in perfect peace, whose mind is stayed on Thee.

482   Jesus Set the World to Singing

A.H.A.

A. H. ACKLEY.

Je - sus set the world to singing when He came, And the song is growing

sweeter, praise His name! Then take up the glad re-frain, Till the

King of Love shall reign; Je-sus set the world to singing when He came.

483 Come in, Holy Spirit Divine

A. S. F. Horne.

Geoffrey R. Palmer.

Come in, Ho-ly Spi-rit di-vine, In this pre - sent
mo-ment of time; Fill my life with Thy pow'r, Bless Thy
ser - vant this hour,— Come in, Ho-ly Spi-rit di - vine.

484 Saviour, Guide Me

G.J.J.

G J. Jones.

Sa - viour, guide me, Sa - viour, guide me, This my
con - stant prayer shall be; For I need Thee to di-

rect me in the paths of li - ber - ty. . . . . Sa - viour,

guide me, Sa - viour, guide me Till I reach e - ter - ni - ty.

485 **Look Through to God**

E. C. W. BOULTON.   MARJORIE HELVER.

1. If your heart with care is press'd Look thro' to God! And you're tempted
2. If your soul is gripp'd by fear, Look thro' to God! And it seems no
3. Are there strong and subtle foes, Look thro' to God! And a host of
4. On the throne is One who knows, Look thro' to God! Ev - 'ry hid-den

and dis-tress'd, Look thro' to God! Not a moment but He's there.
help is near, Look thro' to God! Throw your-self up - on the Lord.
threaten'd woes? Look thro' to God! He will cause thy heart to sing,
tear that flows, Look thro' to God! In His arms He'll hold thee fast,

Ev - 'ry burden He will share, You will find relief in pray'r, Look thro' to God!
All you need in Him is stor'd, You can trust His holy Word, Look thro' to God!
And perform the promis'd thing, You shall mount on faith's strong wing, Look thro' to God!
Till the storms of life are past, Thou shalt reach thy goal at last, Look thro' to God!

I am not under Law

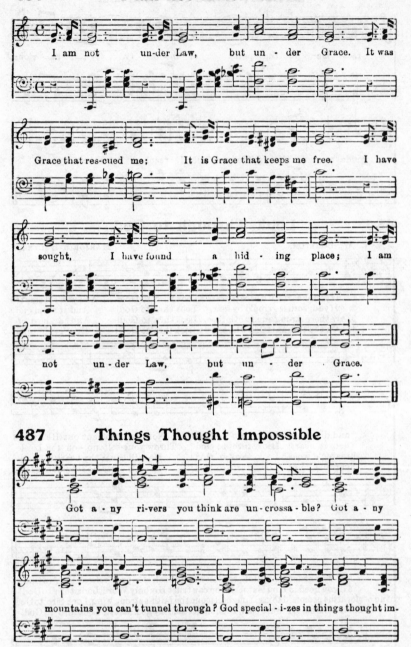

I am not un-der Law, but un-der Grace. It was

Grace that res-cued me; It is Grace that keeps me free. I have

sought, I have found a hid - ing place; I am

not un - der Law, but un - der Grace.

487 Things Thought Impossible

Got a - ny ri - vers you think are un - crossa - ble? Got a - ny

mountains you can't tunnel through? God special - i-zes in things thought im.

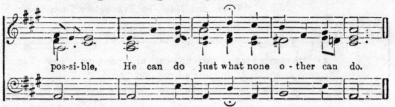

pos-si-ble,   He can do just what none o - ther can do.

488   Thine Alone

J. M. B.   JEANETTE McNEAL BRISSEY.

SOLO, OR VOICES IN UNISON.

O Christ,   my Lord,   I would be lost in Thee,   As

drops of rain from summer show'rs Are lost within the boundless sea; Oh,

may   Thy will   my life, my be-ing own: En-

fold me, hold me, till my-self be Thine a - lone.

489   Evening Vesper

Words and Music by Evangelist Thos. Kemp.

As the ev'n-ing steals up-on us, grant us now Thy

peace, Breathe Thy be-ni-dic-tion on us, from all

care re-lease. Guard and keep us safe this night, May
*Bless our boys on land and sea, Pro-

we Thy glo-ry share; And fold each waiting soul to Thee, With-
tect them in the air;

in Thy ten-der care. A-men, A-men, A--men.

(Used by permission. Happy Heart Gospel Press, Liverpool, 14.)

Elim Publishing Company, Ltd., Clapham Crescent, London, S.W.4.—21697

Elim Choruses No. 10

490   Jesus means so Much to Me

W.P.L.

WENDELL P. LOVELESS.

While the days grow darker, And the way grows harder, Je-sus means so much to me, (to me), Just to hear His voice, And to feel His hand, Je-sus means so much to me; (to me;) Thro' the times of test-ing, I am sweet-ly rest-ing, And His love-ly face I see, (I see), So let come what-e-ver, He will leave me never, Je-sus means so much to me.

F.G.M.

FRED G. MAGEE, arr. J.H N.T.

He lives for e - ver, No Friend like Him;

He chang - es ne - ver, Sa - - - viour from sin;

He loves for e - ver, Praise Him, with me

we'll live to - geth-er e - ter - nal - - ly.

492 Jesus is the Sweetest Name I know

L.L.

LELA LONG.

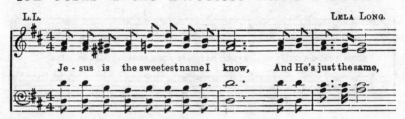

Je - sus is the sweetest name I know, And He's just the same, as His love-ly name, And that's the reas-on why I love Him

so;   Oh,   Je - sus is the sweet-est name I   know.

493   Send Me Forth

B.M. *mp Prayerfully.*   BERT. MITSON.

Send me forth, Lord, bear-ing seed, Wa-tered with my tears.

Con-scious Lord of my great need— O de-stroy my fears;

Send me forth in might and power, Let me preach Thy Word,

Sow-ing dai-ly hour by hour, Till all men have heard.

God's Mighty Ocean

W.S.   *Andante con espress.*   ♩=60.

W. Shepherd.

God's migh-ty o - cean of Love's re-demp-tion,

Waves of com-pass-ion come roll o - ver me; . .

Wash me and cleanse me from all un - like Thee,

Make me a bless-ing wher-e - ver I be.

495   Step by Step with Jesus

Irma Schwartz.

Alda Ryner.

Step by step with Je - sus, He will lead the way, . . .

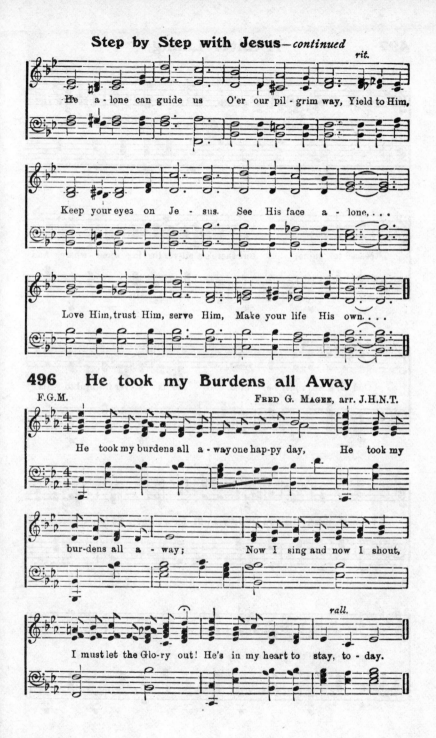

rit.

He a-lone can guide us O'er our pil-grim way, Yield to Him,

Keep your eyes on Je - sus. See His face a - lone,....

Love Him, trust Him, serve Him, Make your life His own....

496 He took my Burdens all Away

F.G.M.

FRED G. MAGEE, arr. J.H.N.T.

He took my burdens all a-way one hap-py day, He took my

bur-dens all a - way; Now I sing and now I shout,

rall.

I must let the Glo-ry out! He's in my heart to stay, to - day.

A Silver Lining

B.M.

Bert Mitson.

Oftentimes the clouds are dark and low'r - ing, It seems the sun has ceased to shine; But there's a sil-ver lin - ing some - where, And God is always just be - hind. He is e - ver faithful to His pro - mise, His own He ne -ver will for - sake; So forward press with courage Till the gladsome day in glo - ry breaks.

Wonderful, Counsellor

B.M.   *mf Not too fast.*

BERT MITSON.

Won - der - ful, Coun - sellor, Sa - viour Di - vine, The whole world waits for you. . . . . . Won - der - ful, Coun - sell - or, Sa - viour Di - vine, The whole world waits for you. . . . . . You be - came so poor to make o - thers rich, Some day they'll un - der - stand. . . . Won - der - ful, Coun - sel - lor Sa - viour Di - vine, The whole world waits for you. . . . .

499 On the Victory Side

W.J.M.

W. J. MAIN.

On the vic - t'ry side, On the vic - t'ry side;

No foe can daunt me, No fear can haunt me, On the vic - t'ry side.

On the vic - t'ry side, On the vic - t'ry side; With

Christ with - in, the fight we'll win, On the vic - t'ry side.

500 Every Moment of Every Day

N.J.C.

NORMAN J. CLAYTON.

On - ly to be what He wants me to be, Ev-'ry moment of ev-'ry

day; ... Yield-ed complete-ly to Je - sus a - lone, Ev-'ry

Every Moment of Every Day—*continued*

step of this pil - grim way; Just to be clay in the Pot-ter's hands,

Rea - dy to do what His word com-mands, On - ly to be what He

wants me to be, Ev - 'ry mo - ment of ev - 'ry day. . . .

501   Breath of Mount Calvary

H.M.   HUGH MITCHELL.

Breath of Mount Cal - v'ry, breathe up-on me, Re - fresh-ing

wind of God's pu - ri - ty, Sweep o'er my soul now

set-ting me free, Breath of Mount Cal - v'ry, breathe up-on me

That I may know Him

L.H.B.

Lee H. Baum.

That I may know Him, Je-sus my Sa - viour, That I may know Him,

Je-sus my Lord . . . , That I may know Him, when in temp-ta - tions,

He's my de-liv-'rer, the liv-ing Word, ... That I may know Him,
the liv-ing Word,

In winning o - thers from sin and dark-ness to Je-sus bring, . That I may

know Him, in re-sur-rec-tion, That I may know Him, as reigning King.

Words and Music by T. Thompson.   Arr. by W. H. Harvey.

S-A-V-I-O-U-R; We want you all to know He's the

One, the on-ly One, who saves from sin, ... If in Him you will be-

lieve, His par-don you'll re-ceive, In His word, His precious word, He tells us

so; . . . . . It was on Cal-va-ry He was nail'd to the tree, And sal-

va-tion was purchas'd that day. . . . . S-A-V-I-O-U-R; We

want you all to know He's the One, the on-ly One, who saves from sin.

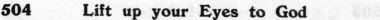

504   Lift up your Eyes to God

H.M.

HUGH MITCHELL.

Lift up your eyes .. to God when your spirit is sad, ...

Lift up your eyes ... to God when your heart is glad; ...

From Zi - on's sa - cred hill, ... There's peace and com - fort still; ...

Lift up, ... Lift up ... your eyes to God. ...

505   There is Victory for me

H.M.

To be sung with assurance.

HUGH MITCHELL.

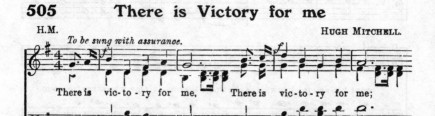

There is vic - to - ry for me, There is vic - to - ry for me;

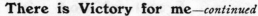
There is Victory for me—*continued*

In the blood of Christ my Sa-viour, There is vic-to-ry for me;

For me, yes, me, for me, yes, me, In the

Blood of Christ my Sa-viour, there is vic-to-ry.

506   For God so loved the World

FRANCES TOWNSEND.   ALFRED B. SMITH.

For God so lov'd the world, He gave His on-ly Son, To die on Calv'ry's

tree, From sin to set me free; Some day He's com-ing back, What

glo-ry that will be! Won-der-ful His love to me.

Breath of God

B.M. *Devotionally.*

BERT MITSON.

mp
Breath of God, breathe on me, Pu - ri - fy my heart;

Fill me, thrill me, through and through, Re - fin - ing ev - 'ry part.

Swing Low

Slow.

Swing low, sweet cha - ri - ot, Com-ing for to car - ry me

home; Swing low, sweet cha - ri - ot, Com-ing for to car - ry me home.
ho e:

FINE.

1. I look'd o-ver Jordan and what did I see, Coming for to car-ry me home? A
2. If you get . . there be-fore . . I do, Coming for to car-ry me home; Tell
3. I'm sometimes up, . . I'm sometimes down, Coming for to car-ry me home: But

Swing Low—*continued*

D.C.

band of an-gels com-ing af-ter me, Coming for to car-ry me home.
all my friends I'm com - ing .. too, Coming for to car-ry me home.
still my soul feels hea-ven-ly . bound, Coming for to car-ry me home.

509   **A Clean Heart**

REV. WALTER G. SMITH.

FRED. H. BYSHE.

Andante con espressione.

So wash me, Thou without, with-in, Or purge with fire, if that must be;
Wash me, Thou, with - out, within, Or purge with fire, if that must be;

No mat-ter how, if on - ly sin Die out in me, die out in me.
A-ny-how, if on-ly sin Die out in me, die out, die out in me.

Die in me,

rit.

rit.

510   At Thy Feet, my Lord

Q. F. THOMPSON.

With feeling. · Not too slow. (Melody in Alto part.)

RON. JONES.

At Thy feet, my Lord, I fall, Just as I am, sin-stressed and torn. Breathe oh, breathe in-to my soul, That heal - ing balm might o'er me roll. Oh, bend me, draw me, Lord, I pray, Un-til a cap-tive soul I lay: Then in heav'n-ly ec-sta-sy I'll love and wor - ship on - ly Thee.

511 Some Golden Daybreak

C.A.B.

Carl A. Blackmore (*arr.* by W. G. Hathaway).

Some gold-en day-break, Je - sus will come, . . .

Some gold-en day-break, Bat - tles all won, . . .

We'll shout the vic-t'ry, . . Break through the blue, . . Some gold-en

day-break, For me, for you. . . . Won't it be wonderful

there, - . . . Hav-ing no burdens to bear? . . Joy-bells all

ringing, with an-gels all singing, O won't it be wonderful there? . .

512 Thank you, Lord, for your many Blessings

Thank you, Lord; Thank you, Lord, for your ma-ny bless-ings, so

full and free. Thank you, Lord; Thank you, that you e-ver thought of

me. Ma-ny ma-ny blessings Thou hast gi-ven un-to me,

Grace is e-ver flowing like a might-y sea. O I want to thank you,

for your love to me. Thank you, Lord, thank you.

513 Thou Healest Yet

Ian MacPherson.

Hugh Mitchell.

O Thou healest yet, tho' the sun be set On the Ga-li-le-an hills;

Thou Healest Yet—*continued*

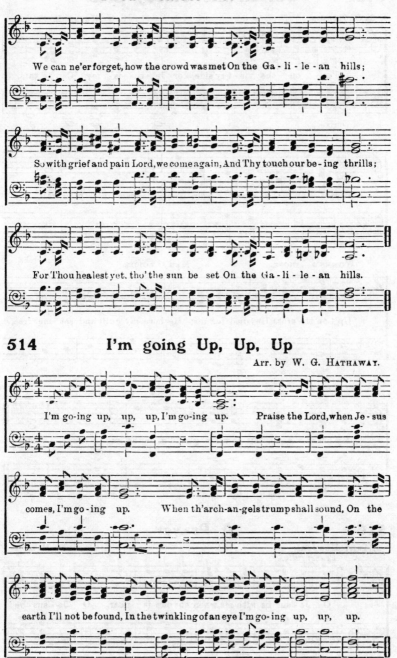

We can ne'er forget, how the crowd was met On the Ga-li-le-an hills;

So with grief and pain Lord, we come again, And Thy touch our be-ing thrills;

For Thou healest yet, tho' the sun be set On the Ga-li-le-an hills.

514 I'm going Up, Up, Up

Arr. by W. G. HATHAWAY.

I'm go-ing up, up, up, I'm go-ing up. Praise the Lord, when Je-sus

comes, I'm go-ing up. When th'arch-an-gels trump shall sound, On the

earth I'll not be found, In the twinkling of an eye I'm go-ing up, up, up.

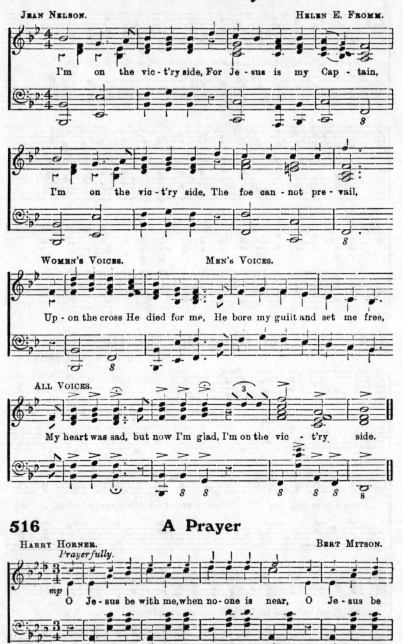

515 I'm on the Vict'ry Side

Jean Nelson.

Helen E. Fromm.

I'm on the vic-t'ry side, For Je-sus is my Cap - tain,

I'm on the vic-t'ry side, The foe can-not pre - vail,

WOMEN'S VOICES.   MEN'S VOICES.

Up-on the cross He died for me, He bore my guilt and set me free,

ALL VOICES.

My heart was sad, but now I'm glad, I'm on the vic - t'ry side.

516 A Prayer

Harry Horner.

Bert Mitson.

Prayerfully.

mp O Je-sus be with me, when no-one is near, O Je-sus be

A Prayer—*continued*

with me in sick-ness and fear, O Je-sus sup-port me when

down with life's strain, O Je-sus give strength for Thy 'Well done' to gain.

517   **God is Love**

COLIN STERNE.

H. ERNEST NICHOL, MUS. BAC., OXON.

pp

Fair-er than ev-'ning splen-dour, Deep-er than sun-set glow,

Clos-er than love by friendship wove, Greater than thought can know;

pp

Sweeter than mu-sic ten-der, Brighter than stars a-bove, ..

mf   *poco rit.*   *ppp*

Such is the love of God in Christ, For God is love. ..

518 The Vale of Contentment

N.J.C.   Norman J. Clayton.

In the beau-ti-ful vale of con-tent-ment, . . Let us walk with the Shep-herd to - day; . . . . . . And the soul will be blest In the val-ley of rest, As we fol-low each step of the way; . . . . On His pleasant green plains He will pas-ture, . . And where wa-ters flow pure He will lead, ... In the beau-ti-ful vale of con - tent-ment and glad-ness, Our Shepherd pro-vides ev -'ry need. . . . . .

519 Thank You, Lord, for saving my Soul!

MR. & MRS. S.S.   MR. & MRS. SETH SYKES.

Thank you, Lord, for sav-ing my soul; Thank you, Lord, for making me whole;

Thank you, Lord, for giv-ing to me Thy great sal-va-tion so rich and free.

520   The Highway Home

A.A.L.   A. A. LUTHER.

I'm on the high-way home, . I'm on the high-way home. The

Mas-ter spoke my name, He call'd me and I came; I'm on the high-way

home, . I'm on the high-way home, . I'm on the high-way home. 'O

come and go with me To my Father's house;' I'm on the high-way home.

521 ## Witnessing for Jesus

MILDRED McQUEEN.　　　　　　　　　　WENDELL P. LOVELESS.

Wit-nessing for Je - sus, I'm tell-ing of His love,

Wit-nessing for Je - sus, From earth to heav'n a - bove, Hal-le-

lu-jah, with His pre-sence al - ways with me and His joy to fill my

soul, I'm wit-ness-ing for Je-sus till I reach my heav'nly goal.

522 ## Saved to tell Others

Hollywood Gospel Team.　　　　　　　　ARTHUR WOOLSEY.

We're Sav'd, Sav'd to tell o - thers of the Man of Ga - li - lee. . . .

Saved, Sav'd to live dai - ly for the Christ of Cal - va - ry. . . . .

rit.

Saved, Sav'd to in - vite you to His sal - va - tion free.... We're

Saved, Saved, Saved by His blood for all e - ter - ni - ty.....

523 Saved am I, and Satisfied

G. R. P.　　　　　　　　GEOFFREY R. PALMER. Arr. by W.G.H.

O saved am I and sa - tis-fied in Je - sus Christ my King;

His ri - sen pow'r with - in my life, the pow'r that con - quers sin.

His love di - vine en - cir - cles me with the rich - es of His

grace, But best of all I'll see .. Him face to face.

524 The One Who loves me

L. J. RICHARDS.

GEOFFREY R. PALMER, arr. by W.G.H.

The One who loves me so is Je - sus, He died to set me
free; ..... And now in Him I'm re - joic - - ing, He's
paid my pe - nal - ty. ..... On Cal -v'ry's cru-el cross He
suf - fered, And died that all might live; .... That ev - 'ry
soul who on Je - sus be-lieves Might e - ver-last-ing life re - ceive. ....

525 Jesus, Thy Lovely Name

B.C.M.

B. C. MARTIN, arr. by T. L. HARGRAVE.

Je - sus, Thy love - ly Name has ban-ish'd all my fear; ....

No o-ther Name to me could e-ver be so dear; ..

Thy true-est joy and peace brings heav'n on earth to me; ....

Thy love be-got-ten bonds are sweet-est li-ber-ty......

526 ## Calvary Love

Rev. E. T. Gurr.   Geoffrey R. Palmer, arr. by W.G H.

Cal-va-ry love flow o-ver me, Nothing of self, but all of Thee;

rit.

Christ of the Cross, a-bide in me, O fill me with Cal-v'ry love.

527 **Jesus my Lord**

L. J. RICHARDS.

GEOFFREY R. PALMER, arr. by W.G.H.

Je-sus my Lord, Sa-viour a-dored, Help me to walk with Thee; ..

Seeking the lost what-e-ver the cost, Thine all the glo-ry shall be.....

528 Pray, O Pray, as Christ commanded you

L.A.O.

L. A. OUTHRED.

Pray, O pray, as Christ commanded you; Pray for pow'r, great things for God to do;

Pray al-ways for help and guidance too; Pray, pray, pray....

Pray to God when ev'rything goes wrong, Pray for strength when trials are hard and long;

Pray for joy, 'till in your heart's a song; Pray, pray, pray.

529 I want to See Him

R.H.C.

R. H. CORNELIUS.

O I want to see Him, look up-on His face, There to sing for e - ver
of His sav - ing grace... On the streets of glo - ry let me lift my
voice; Cares all past, home at last, E - ver to re - joice...

530 I Love Thee

B.A.B.

Worshipfully.

B. A. BAUR; With acknowledgement to
'Marcheta' by VICTOR SCHERTZINGER.

My Je - sus, I love Thee, I love Thee, I do; My Je - sus, I
love Thee, I love Thee, I do; Thy beau-ty en-thralls me, Thy
love has ffll'd my soul; My Je - sus, I love Thee, I love Thee, I do.

531

I no Longer Choose

A.E.S.

A. E. STRINGER; Harmonised by P. RONAN.

I no longer choose my path-way,.... I no longer plan my day,..... For Je-sus is my light and sun-shine;.. Je-sus is my life, my way,.... I can hear His voice of guid-ance .. As I fol-low Him each day; ... He will lead me right, Through the darkest night, Till the morning dawns for aye. ....

532

There is a Fight

B.C.M. *Martial emphasis.*

B. C. MARTIN; Arr. by T. HARGRAVE.

There is a fight we all are in, 'Tis the cease-less fight with sin;

There is a Fight—*continued*

This is the fight we all may win With Je - sus as our King; So
as our King;

press on, and pray on, Join bat - tle with the foe; De -

fend the right in Christ our might, Then Vic - t'ry shall we know.

533 ## Jesus is the One

Slowly and Tenderly.

Arr. by RON JONES.

Je - sus is the One, yes, He's the on - ly One; Let Him have His

way un - til the day is done, When He speaks you know the

clouds will have to go, Just because He loves you so. . . . . .

534   Oh! Say, but I'm Glad

Rev. Jas. Sullivan.

Mildred E. Sullivan.

Oh! say, but I'm glad, I'm glad, Oh! say, but I'm glad,

{ Je-sus has tak-en my sins all a-way; }
{ Je-sus has come and my cup'so-ver-run; } Oh! say, but I'm glad.

535   Good-night

F.G.M.

Fred G. Magee.

Good - night, Good-night, The Lord watch between you and me; ...

Good - night, Good - night, His peace and His love rest with thee; ..

Keep thee, bless thee, And guard thee till morning is light; .

Race run, Crown won, No more to say Good-night. ..

Elim Publishing Company, Ltd., Clapham Crescent, London, S.W.4.—21698

Elim Choruses, No. 11

536 Since the Fulness of His Love Came In

E. E. HEWITT.   B. D. ACKLEY.

I can nev-er tell how much I love Him I can nev-er tell His love for

me; For it pas-seth hu-man meas-ure, Like a

deep, un-fath-om'd sea;   'Tis redeem-ing love in Christ my

deep, unfathom'd sea;

Sav-iour,   In my soul the heav'nly joys be-gin;   And I

live for Je-sus on-ly, Since the ful-ness of His love came in.

How I Love Thee, My Saviour

M.D.

MERRILL DUNLOP.

How I love Thee, my Sav-iour, Thou art the Light of my way; .... Thou dost watch o'er me dai - ly, And Thou dost hear when I pray, ... Thou didst die for me on dark Cal - va - ry, Paid sin's pen - al - ty Just to set me free; Thou wilt walk with me Till Thy face I shall see Some glo - rious day ....

It Is Wonderful

A.P.R.

A. P. ROBINS.

It is won-der-ful to walk with Je-sus, In the light of His word. It will give you peace and sat-is - fac-tion, come a- long and walk with Him. Come a - long, come a - long you can join in our song; It will give you peace and sat - is - fac-tion come a - long and walk with Him.

I'm Following the Master

HUGH MITCHELL.

I'm fol-low-ing the Mas-ter, I'm fol-low-ing the Lord, I'm keeping close to Jesus and I'm trusting in His word; He leads me by His Spirit, He cleans-es by His Blood, I'm keep-ing close to Je-sus and I'm trusting in His word; What-ev-er be my pathway, in sunshine or in rain, I know my life is safe with Him, I know the end is gain; I'm fol-low-ing the Mas-ter, I'm fol-low-ing the Lord, I'm

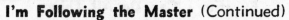

keep - ing close to Je - sus and I'm trust-ing in His word.

540 **Christ for Me**

A.B.   ALEX BURNS.

Christ   for   me, ...   yes, it's Christ   for

1st time.

me, ...   He's   my Saviour, my Lord   and King;

2nd time.

I'm   so hap-py I shout and sing;   E - v'ry day as I

go   my way it is Christ   for   me. . , .

By Him I Can Do All Things

F.M.

FRANCES MORRISON.

Con spirito.

mf By Him I can do all things, All things, all things, Though I'm feel-ing for-sa - - - ken, weak, and in dis-tress. . . . . . . By Him I can do all things, All things, all things, For He comes to de-li - ver, strength-en, cheer and bless. . . . . . .

8ve.

542   Exceeding Abundantly

H.F.L.

H. F. LANCE.

Ex-ceed-ing a-bun-dant-ly, That is God's way, Sur-pass-ing what-
-ev-er we think or we say, Sup-ply-ing His chil-dren with
grace day by day, Ex-ceed-ing a-bun-dant-ly, All thro' life's way.

543   The "Goodbye" Chorus

W.P.L.

WENDELL P. LOVELESS.

Good-bye, our God is watching o'er you, Good-bye, His
mer-cy goes be-fore you. Good-bye, and we'll be praying
for you so good-bye, may God bless you..............

544 Somewhere Beyond the Blue

A.B.S.

ALFRED B. SMITH.

Some-where beyond the blue there's a man-sion for me, Somewhere beyond the
blue I am long-ing to be; I'll see my Saviour's face and
sing of saving grace, Somewhere beyond the blue, some day......

545 Step by Step

BUD METZGER.

MAXINE ANDERSON.

Step by step I'll fol-low Je - sus, Hour by hour I'm in His
care. Day by day He walks be - side me,
Thro' the years I'll know He's there, He can still the might - y

Step by Step (continued)

tem - pest, He can calm the troubled sea, He the wa-ters trod,

He's the Son of God, He's the One who al-ways walks with me.

546   Long, Long Ago

N.J.C.   NORMAN J. CLAYTON.

Long, long a - go, ... Long, long a - go, ...

Je - sus paid sins pen - al - ty On the Cross of Cal - va - ry;

Long, long a - go, ... Long, long a - go, ...

Je - sus died that sinners might live, Long, long a - go. ....

Take Fresh Heart

FRANCES MORRISON.

Je-sus will ne-ver for-sake you, So take fresh

heart,..... Je-sus will ne-ver for-sake you, So

take fresh heart...... Though you may in temp-ta - tion

be, He is a - ble to suc - cour thee, Trust in

Je - sus con - tin - u - 'lly, And take fresh heart.....

Don't Go in the Valley

R.J.

RON. JONES.

Don't go in the val-ley of des-pair, When the Dev-il hits you low! Go to Christ in pray'r, Leave your bur-den there, Talk to Him Who loves you so. Leave it there, leave it there! Leave your hea-vy bur-den there, Go to Christ in pray'r Leave your bur-den there, Talk to Him who loves you so.

Leave it there,

Leave it there,

Leave your burden there,

549 Morning Glory

S.E.C.

SIDNEY E. COX.

There'll be glo - ry in the morning, When we meet on heaven's shore,

There'll be glo - ry in the morn-ing, When we meet to part no more.

When our trav'lling days are ov - er, And we en - ter thro' the door,

There'll be glo - ry in the morning, When we meet on heaven's gold-en shore.

550 Jesus, I Love

A. RACE.

MOLLY RACE.

Je - sus, I love to sing Thy name, No name so sweet as Thine;

These gen-tle words should raise my song To notes al - most di - vine.

551 I Love to Hear His Voice

W.P.L.

WENDELL P. LOVELESS.

O, I love to hear His voice, His voice, Saying, "you be-long to Me, to Me.

You are not your own, With a price you're bought, And you're mine e - ter-nal - ly."

And I love to hear Him say, Him say, "I have saved you by my grace, my grace, And

when I get to glo-ry it will then be grander still, for I shall see His face.

552 Jesus, How Wonderful Thou Art

J.W.H.

J. W. HALL.

1. Je - sus, how wonderful Thou art; Je - sus, Thy love hath won my heart;
2. Purge me, and put Thy fire within; Use me to fight the pow'r of sin;

1st time.   2nd time.

Jesus, From Thee I'll ne'er depart, Je-sus, my Lord.
Fill me with love that I might win   Someone for Thee.

Jesus

R.J.

RON. JONES.

Je - sus, Je - sus, Je - sus, Fair - est of the
fair,.................... Je - sus, Je - sus, Je - sus,
None with Thee com - pare:................ Help me, Lord, to be
like Thee, Help me Thine im-age to bear,................ Show-ing the
world the fra - grance Of Thy beau - ty rare.................

554

In the Rock, I'll Hide

J.E.A.

JOHN E. ABNETT.

In the Rock, I'll hide, In the sha-dow a - bide; And when the

The Rock. I'll hide,

storms of life come sweeping ov - er me In the Rock I'll hide.

555

His Love is Wonderful to Me

P.W. *Espressivo.*

PAUL WHITE.

His love is won - derful to me, ... His love is

won-derful to me; . . For Je-sus loved me so, He did to

Calv'ry go; His love is won - der - ful to me.

556 He Holds My Hand

N.J.C.

NORMAN J. CLAYTON.

He holds my hand, . . Je - sus holds my hand; . .

Safely to heaven He leads the way, He is my keeper from day to day;

He holds my hand, . . Je - sus holds my hand; . . The

rit.

road may be long, But my Saviour is strong, And He holds my hand.

557 With God All Things Are Possible

J.W.H.

J. W. HALL.

With God all things are pos - si - ble, This is my theme and song; With

God, a blessed part-nership, A u-nion sure and strong. Linked

up with God the Fa-ther Thro' Je-sus Christ the Son, All

things are pos-si-ble to those who put their trust in God.

558 Standing Somewhere in the Shadows*

E.J.R. *Tenderly and with feeling.* E. J. ROLLINGE.

Standing somewhere in the shadows you'll find Je - sus, He's the

Friend who al-ways cares and un-der-stands. Standing somewhere in the

shadows you will find Him, And you'll know Him by the nail-prints in His hands.

*Specially arranged as sung in Elim Revival Campaigns.

The Meeting in the Air

M.T.R.

MAY TAYLOR ROBERTS.

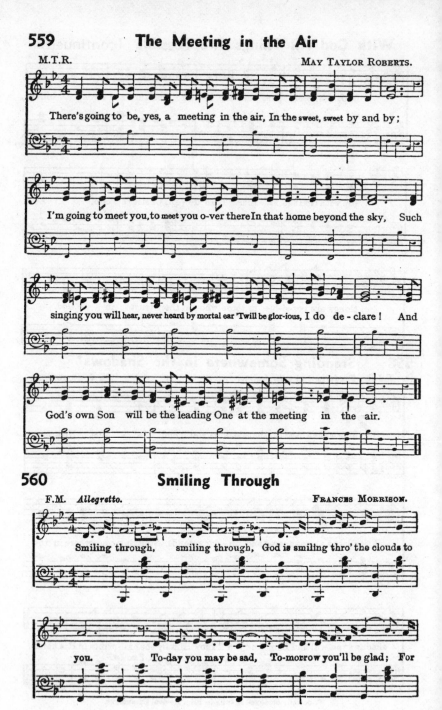

There's going to be, yes, a meeting in the air, In the sweet, sweet by and by;

I'm going to meet you, to meet you o-ver there In that home beyond the sky, Such

singing you will hear, never heard by mortal ear 'Twill be glor-ious, I do de-clare! And

God's own Son will be the leading One at the meeting in the air.

560

Smiling Through

F.M. *Allegretto.*

FRANCES MORRISON.

Smiling through, smiling through, God is smiling thro' the clouds to

you. To-day you may be sad, To-morrow you'll be glad; For

Smiling Through (continued)

Jesus never fails, His love is true. Smiling through, smiling

through, There are brighter days ahead for you, Though clouds be o-ver

cast, They'll roll away at last, For God is smil-ing, smil-ing through.

561   He Is Lovely

R.D.

ROBERT DODDS.

For He is love-ly, Yes, He is love-ly, The Christ of

God is fair-er than the sun, than the sun, For He is love-ly, Yes, He is

love-ly, The Christ of God is fair-er than the sun.

All Because of Calvary

All my sins are gone .... All because of Cal - va — ry;
All my sins are gone,

Life is fill'd with song,........ All because of Cal - va - ry;
Life is fill'd with song,

Christ my Sav - iour lives, Lives from sin to set me free;
Christ my Sav-iour lives,

Some day He's coming, O wondrous, blessed day, All, yes, all be-cause of Cal - va - ry.

563 **Make Me a Blessing**

Geo B. Schulyer

Make me a bless - ing, Make me a bless - ing,

rit.

Out of my life.......... May Je - sus shine; ......
Out of my life

MEN.

UNISON.
WOMEN

Make me a bless .. ing, O Sav .. iour, I pray, ...
I pray Thee, my Sav - iour.

PARTS.
ad lib

Make me a bless .. ing to some - one to - day. ....

564

He Cannot Fail

C.E.M. JR.
C. E. MASON, JR.

He cannot fail, for He is God, He cannot fail, He pledged His Word;

He cannot fail, He'll see you thro', He cannot fail, He'll an-swer you.

Fix Your Eyes Upon Him

N.J.C.

Norman J. Clayton.

When the road is rough and steep, Fix your eyes upon Je - sus,

He a - lone has pow'r to keep, Fix your eyes upon Him;

Je - sus is a gracious Friend, One on whom you can de - pend,

He is faith - ful to the end, Fix your eyes upon Him.

566   We Are Pressing On To Victory

J.W.H.

J. W. Hall.

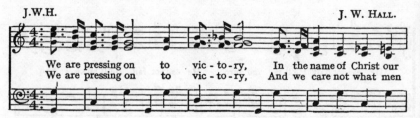

We are pressing on to vic - to - ry, In the name of Christ our
We are pressing on to vic - to - ry, And we care not what men

We Are Pressing On to Victory (continued)

Lord,   And w'ere go - ing on,   to   glo - ry   and   the
say,   We would hear "well done" when our course   is   run   on

1st time   2nd time   FINE.

Great Re - ward,   that Great Day.

567   God Is Love

I.R.
ISABELLE RITTER.

Seedtime and harvest and soft sum-mer breeze, tell us God   is   love;

Sweet scented flowers and birds in the trees say that God   is   love;

Moon shining down in its splen - dour,   Star-light in hea-vens a - bove,

They tell of His might, and all thro' the night say that God   is   love.

My Story

J.W.H.

J. W. HALL.

1. How I love to tell the sto - ry   Of the Lord who came from
2. He's the au - thor of my sto - ry,   And I sing His praise and

glo - ry,   How He saved me,   and healed me,   And
glo - ry,   Mighty Heal - er,   Bap - ti - ser,   And

1st time.   ‖ *2nd time.*

gave me pewor with - in.

glo - rious com-ing King.

Walking With Jesus

C.H.L.

*In moderate time. *(Melody in lower notes.)*

C. HAROLD LOWDEN.

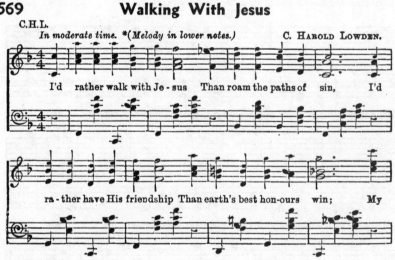

I'd   rather walk with Je - sus   Than roam the paths of   sin,   I'd

ra - ther have His friendship Than earth's best hon-ours   win;   My

Walking with Jesus (continued)

one de-sire to please Him As dai-ly ways we trod. And so we're walking onward, upward, Bound for Heav'n—*and God!*

*Beautiful two-part effect is obtainable by having Sopranos take middle notes.

570   Jesus is the Sweetest Name I Know

M. D.

Not too fast

Merrill Dunlop

Je-sus is the sweetest name that I have ev-er heard;
Je-sus is the sweet-est name that I have ev-er heard;
ev-er heard;

Sweet-er to this heart of mine than an-y oth-er word; When He speaks my
an-y oth-er word;

soul de-light-eth, for I love Him so; Yes, Je-sus is the sweetest name I know.

Cheer up, ye saints of God, There's nothing to wor-ry a-bout,
Nothing to make you feel a-fraid; Nothing to make you doubt; Re-
mem-ber Je-sus nev-er fails, So why not trust Him and shout! You'll be
sor-ry you wor-ried at all to-mor-row morn - ing.

H.G.

HELEN GRIGGS.

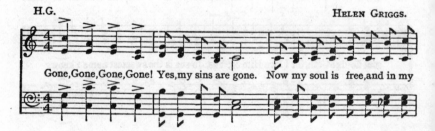

Gone, Gone, Gone, Gone! Yes, my sins are gone. Now my soul is free, and in my

My Sins are Gone (continued)

heart's a song; Bur-ied in the deepest sea, Yea, that's good enough for me;

I shall live e-ter-nal-ly, Praise God! My sins are gone!

573 **Whistle or Sing**

H.D.L. HARRY DIXON LOES.

Whis-tle a tune or sing a song The whole day through;

Cheering you up, 'twill make you strong, Life's work to do.

Others should know what Christ the Lord Has done for you—

Whistle a tune or sing a song The whole day through.

R.J.

RON. JONES.

I am con - tent - ed with Je - sus, I am con - tent - ed with

Him; .... Dai - ly He helps me my bur - den to bear,

Hap - py for He dwells with - in .... I am con - tent - ed with

Je - sus, He's by my side ev - 'ry day, ... In sunshine or

a tempo.

rain, He's always the same, I am con - tented with Him.

575   Rest, Sweet Rest

FRANCES MORRISON.

Rest, sweet rest,..... Come un-to Je-sus and rest;.... Do you feel tired and wea - ry? Does life seem dark and drea - - ry? Rest, sweet rest,..... Come un-to Je - sus and rest,...... Just give Him your heart, And He will im - part His rest, sweet rest.......

Something Happened

A.H.A.

A. H. ACKLEY.

Some-thing hap-pened when He saved me, Happened in my
Something real-ly hap-pened

heart, happened in my heart, Some - thing happened when He
O yes it When He

rit.

saved me, Something happened in my heart.
saved me, when He saved me,

577

If You'll Take My Jesus

E.R.W.

ETHEL R. WILLETS.

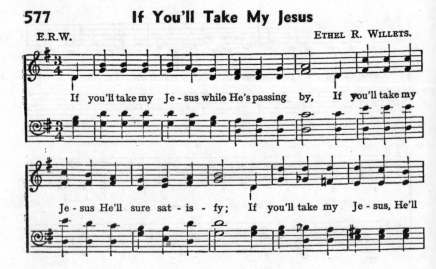

If you'll take my Je - sus while He's passing by, If you'll take my

Je - sus He'll sure sat - is - fy; If you'll take my Je - sus, He'll

If You'll Take My Jesus (continued)

hear your heart's cry; If you'll take my Je - sus { to - day. / to - night }

578 Things Are Different Now

S.W.G.   STANTON W. GAVITT.

Low voices.

Things are dif-f'rent now, Something happened to me When I gave my heart to

High voices.

Je - sus. Things are dif-f'rent now; I was chang'd, it must be, When I
Unison D.S.— Things are dif - f'rent now: Something hap-pened that day When I

FINE.

gave my heart to Him.   Things I loved be - fore have
gave my heart to Him.

Unison.

D.S. al Fine.

passed a - way, Things I loved far more have come to stay.

Some Sweet Day

NORMAN J. CLAYTON.

Some sweet day, by His grace, I shall see Je - sus face to face;

He will come, by and by, And we shall reign with Him for e - ter - ni - ty.

Sha - dows gone, sor - rows past, All will be bless - ed - ness at last;

Morn will break, the night flee a - way, We'll see Je - sus some sweet day.

Elim Publishing Co., Ltd., Clapham Crescent. London, S.W.4.—16752

Elim Choruses, No. 12

Calvary

N.E.G.

Norman E. Good.

Cal-v'ry is the place to find the Sav - iour, Je-sus the
Sav-iour di-vine;.... Tell Him thy sin, Have faith in Him,
Life e-ternal shall be thine...... Cal-v'ry is the place to find the
Sav - iour, Come now and you'll find Him true; 'Twas there His blood He
shed, And then rose from the dead, ev-er-last-ing life to win for you.

I have Christ in my heart

W.P.L.

WENDELL P. LOVELESS.

Martial tempo

What though wars may come, with marching feet and beat of the drum, For

I have Christ in my heart; What though na-tions rage, as

my heart,

we ap-proach the end of the age, For I have Christ in my

heart; God is still on the throne, Al-might - y God is He;

And He cares for His own through all e - ter - ni - ty, So let

come what may, what-ev - er it is, I on - ly say that

I have Christ in my heart (continued)

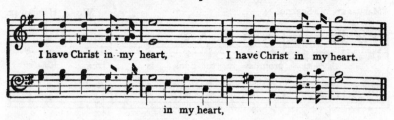

I have Christ in my heart,   I have Christ in my heart.

in my heart,

582   He owns the Cattle on a Thousand Hills

J.W.P.   J. W. PETERSEN.

He owns the cat-tle on a thousand hills, the wealth in ev - 'ry mine.

He owns the riv-ers and the rocks and rills, The sun and stars that shine;

Won - der - ful rich - es more than tongue can tell, He is

my Fa-ther so they're mine as well, He owns the cat-tle on a

thou-sand hills and so I know He cares for me.

583 Every Promise in the Book is True

Margaret W. Scragg.

W. G. Hathaway.

Ev-'ry prom-ise in the Book is true, Ev-'ry
prom-ise in the Book is true, Tho' at times my faith would fail And the
temp-ter would pre-vail, Ev-'ry prom-ise in the Book is true.

584 Summertime in my heart

L. C. J.

Lois C. Johnson.

It is summertime in my heart, Yes, it's summertime in my
heart; Since Je-sus saved me, New life He gave me,
E-ven in win-ter time it's sum-mer in my heart!

It is summer time in my heart, Yes it's sum-mer time in my

heart; Since Je-sus saved me, New life He gave me,

E-ven in win-ter time it's sum-mer in my heart!

It is sum-mertime in my heart, Yes, it's summertime in my

heart; Since Je-sus saved me, New life He gave me,

E-ven in win-ter time it's sum-mer in my heart!

585 Wonderful, so wonderful

ROBERT C. LOVELESS.   WENDELL P. LOVELESS.

Won - der-ful it is that Je - sus came, And died up-on the
Won - der-ful it is He's com - ing soon To take us to Him-

cross for you
-self a - bove   Won - der-ful it is He

rose and lives, Won - der-ful be-cause 'tis true, ...

And we'll live with Him e - ter - nal - ly,

'Tis won - der-ful so won - der - ful. . . . .

The Theme of my Song

H.L.

HALDOR LILLENAS.

He is the love-ly theme of my song, He is my light from a-far;

Glo-ry and praise shall to Him be-long, He is my bright Morning

Star; ...... Strength for my weakness He doth im-part,

He is the joy of my long - ing heart, Fair Rose of Sharon is

Je-sus to me; He is the theme of my song.

Geared and Anchored

ALFRED B. SMITH.
HARRY DIXON LOES.

Unison.

We are geared, geared, geared to the times, But anchored to the Rock;

With no fear, fear, fear of the foe, His ev-'ry move we'll block. To the

world of sin and strife Tell that Christ gives peace and life;

We are geared, geared, geared to the times, But anchored to the Rock!

588

This one thing I know

S.C.
SIDNEY COX.

This one thing I know, This one thing I know,

This one thing I know (continued)

God in great mer - cy par-doned me, Snapped sin's fetters and set me free,

Once I was blind but now I see, This one thing I know.

589   When we see Christ

E.K.R.   ESTHER K. RUSTHOI.

It will be worth it all, . . . When we see Je - sus; Life's trials will

seem so small, when we see Christ; One glimpse of His dear face, all sor-row

will e - rase, . . . so brave-ly run the race, . . . Till we see Christ.

590
N.J.C.

Faithful Forever

Norman J. Clayton.

Faith-ful for ev - er! Je - sus my Friend; Guid-ing, keep-ing,

sat - is - fy - ing To the ver - y end: Sun-shine or shad - ow,

He is the same; Faith-ful for ev - er! O, praise His name.

591
S.E.C.

My Great Unchanging Friend

S. E. Cox.

He's the same to-day as yes-ter-day, My great unchanging Friend;

He's the same to-day as yes-ter-day, Just the same un-to the end;

By His mighty pow'r He holds me, In His arms of love en-folds me;

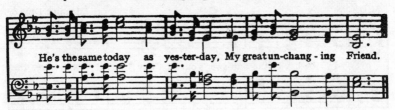

He's the same today as yes-ter-day, My great un-chang - ing Friend.

592   Make me a Jewel

D.J.T.

D. J. THOMAS, A.T.S.C.

Je - sus, Je - sus, make me a jew-el for Thee,

Ev - er shin - ing in Thy bright sunshine of love;

Keep me glist - 'ning that in me oth-ers may see,

I'm a jew - el, found by my Sav-iour a - bove.

593 **I believe the Answer's on the Way**

M.D.

Merrill Dunlop.

I be-lieve the an-swer's on the way; I be-lieve the
Lord has heard me pray; "Cast not a-way your confidence," Saith the Lord our
God. Now by faith in Him a-lone I stand, Firm-ly held by
His al-might-y hand; Ful-ly trusting in His promise, Praise the Lord!

594 **Peace floods my Soul**

W.P.L.

Wendell P. Loveless.

Peace floods my soul for I have the Sav-iour; Peace that He
gives, The world can-not take it a-way; Free-dom from

Peace floods my Soul (continued)

sin, since Je-sus came in, Oh won-der-ful, won-der-ful,

won-der-ful peace, Floods my soul since the Sav-iour came in ....

595 He wants to walk and talk with me

D.B.L.

D. B. LEIGHTNER.

Steady rhythm.

He wants to walk with me Ev-'ry moment of the day..................

He wants to talk with me Ev-'ry moment of the day..................

He wants to work thro' me, bless thro' me, All a-long the way; He wants to

walk with me, talk with me Ev-'ry moment of the day..................

596

Heavenly Sunshine

Rev. H. J. Zelley.

G. B. Cook.

Heav-en-ly sun-shine, heav-en-ly sun-shine, Flood-ing my
soul with glo-ry di-vine; Hal-le lu-jah! I am re-joic-ing, Sing-ing His prais-es, Je-sus is mine.

597

Follow, I will Follow

H. L. & M. W. Brown.

Howard L. Brown.

Fol-low, I will fol-low Thee, My Lord, Fol-low
ev-'ry pass-ing day...... My to-morrows are all
known to Thee, Thou wilt lead me all the way......

598 I have found a wonderful Saviour

Arr. by W. G. HATHAWAY.

1. I have found a won-der-ful Sav-iour, A - men bro-ther, A - men.

He has pardoned my be-hav-iour, A - men brother, A - men.

A-men, brother, A-men, sis-ter, A-men, brother, A - men,

I have found a wonderful Saviour, A-men brother, A - men.

599 Sunshine Corner

Arr. by W. G. HATHAWAY.

Sunshine corner, oh, it's jolly fine, It's for chil-dren un-der ninety-nine.

All are welcome, seats are given free, Elim sunshine corner is the pla.e for me.

600 Then Jesus Came

OSWALD J. SMITH.

HOMER RODEHEAVER.

When Je - sus comes the tempter's pow'r is bro - ken; When Je - sus comes the tears are wiped a - way. He takes the gloom and fills the life with glo - ry, For all is changed when Jesus comes to stay.

601 Somebody else needs Him, too

SUSAN R. PECK.

B. D. ACKLEY.

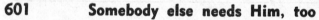

Some-bod-y somewhere, per-haps at your side, Some-one is wait-ing for you; yes, wait-ing for you; Say that for all Je-sus

Somebody else needs Him, too (continued)

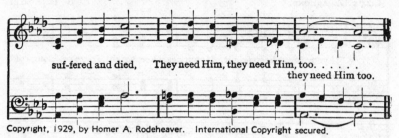

suf-fered and died,   They need Him, they need Him, too. . . . . .

they need Him too.

602   Jesus is the Joy of Living

A.H.A.

REV. A. H. ACKLEY.

Je-sus is the Joy of Liv - ing, He's the King of Life to me ; . . . . . .

of Life to me ;

Un - to Him my all I'm giv - ing, His for ev-er-more to be (to be).

I will do what He com-mands me, An - y-where He leads I'll go (I'll go);

rit. - - - - - -

Je - sus is the Joy of Liv - ing, He's the dear-est Friend I know.

603 **If your heart keeps right**

LIZZIE DE ARMOND.   B. D. ACKLEY.

If your heart keeps right, If your heart keeps right, There's a song of
glad-ness in the dark-est night; If your heart keeps right, If your
heart keeps right, Ev-'ry cloud will wear a rain-bow, If your heart keeps right.

604 **ALONE**

B.H.P.   BEN H. PRICE.

A - lone,   a - lone,   He bore it all a - lone;   He
It was a-lone,   yes, all a-lone,   yes, all a-lone;
gave Himself to save His own,   He suffer'd, bled and died alone, a - lone.

Copyright, 1914, by Homer A. Rodeheaver.   International Copyright secured.

605 There's a way back to God

Eric H. Swinstead.

There's a way back to God from the dark paths of sin; There's a
door that is o-pen and you may go in: At Cal-va-ry's cross is
where you be-gin, When you come as a sin-ner to Je - sus.

606 Calvary is more than All

H.A.C.

H. A. Court.

Cal-va-ry is more than all to me, Cal-va-ry is more than all. . . .
There I had my sins for-giv-en, There I learnt the way to hea - ven.
Cal - va-ry is more than all to me, Yes, Cal-va-ry is more than all. . . .

Arr. by W. G. HATHAWAY.

Je-sus is a wonderful Sav-iour, He will car-ry you thro',

Je-sus is a wonderful Sav-iour, He will carry you thro' my brother

Je-sus is a wonderful Sav-iour, He will car-ry you thro' and when the

battle is done and the vic-tory's won, my Lord will carry you thro', my loving

bro-ther .... when the world is on fire .... you'll need my

Je - sus .... to be your Sav - iour .... He'll ev - er

Jesus is a wonderful Saviour (continued)

hide you .... in the rock of a - ges, ... The rock of

rit. pp

a - ges .... that was cleft for you, That was cleft for you.

608   **He gives me satisfying peace**

N.J.C.   Norman J. Clayton.

He gives me sat - is - fy-ing peace; This wonderful Sav - iour,

He gives me joys that nev - er cease; This wonderful Lord,

'Tis on - ly Je - sus who can bless with ev - er - last-ing hap - pi-

- ness, And He's my Sav - iour, This wonderful Lord.

There's a deep, deep peace

Arr. by W. G. HATHAWAY.

There's a deep, deep, peace, dwelling in my heart, Telling of my Saviour's love for me There's a deep, deep, peace, dwelling in my heart, Tell-ing of my Saviour's love for me, His prom-is-es . . . they shall never fail, They shall never fail, Oh, They shall never fail, There's a deep, deep, peace, dwelling in my heart, Telling of my Saviour's love for me.

(Hallelujah)
(Oh glo-ry)
(Hallelujah)

610

They that sow in tears

Psalm 126.

Eileen Batch.

They that sow in tears, Go-ing forth with weeping; Bearing precious seed, While the world lies sleep-ing: Doubtless shall re-turn, Bringing in their sheaves: Praising God with joy for harvest reap - ing.

611

I want to live right

Spirituel.

Arr. by W. G. Hathaway.

I want to live right, that God may use me, at an-y-time and an-y-where. I want to live right that God may use me at an-y-time and an-y-where.

If you want joy

Arr. by W. G. HATHAWAY.

If you want joy, real joy, won-der-ful joy, let Je-sus come in-to your heart. If you want joy, real joy, won-der-ful joy, let Je-sus come in-to your heart. Your sin's He'll take a-way, your night He'll turn to day, Your heart He'll make o-ver a-new and then come in to stay. If you want joy, real

If you want joy (continued)

joy, won-der-ful joy, let Je-sus come in-to your heart.

613   The windows of Heaven are open

Arr. by W. G. Hathaway.

The win-dows of heav-en are o-pen, The bless-ings are fall-ing to-night; There's joy, joy, joy in my heart, For Je-sus made ev-'ry-thing right. I gave Him my old tat-tered gar-ment, He gave me a robe of pure white; I'm feast-ing on man-na from heav-en, and that's why I'm hap-py to-night.

Christit is the answer

Air by Major T. W. MALTBY
Arr. by Major W. E. BEARCHELL.

T.W.M.

Christ is the an - swer to my ev -'ry need; Christ is the

BASS. to my ev -'ry need;

an - swer, He is my Friend in-deed. Prob - lems of life my

He is my Friend in-deed.

spi-rit may as - sail, With Christ my Sa - viour I shall nev-er

Sa - viour

fail, For Christ— is the an - swer to my need.

By permission of the Salvation Army International Music Board.

615

Give me oil in my lamp

Arr. by W. G. HATHAWAY.

Give me oil in my lamp, keep me burn-ing, Give me oil in my lamp I

pray, Give me oil in my lamp, keep me burn-ing, Keep me

burn-ing till the break of day; Sing Ho-san - na,

sing Ho-san - na, Sing Ho-san-a to the King of Kings:

Sing Hosan - na, sing Hosan - na, sing Ho-san-na to our King.

Open wide the door

A.E.K.

A. E. KELLY.

Allegretto. mf.

O-pen wide the door of your heart to Je-sus let Him en-ter in to-day;

Open wide the door of your heart to Him and evermore with you He'll stay,

mp

He will cleanse your heart from the stain of sin and keep you in the narrow way,

f

Let Him reign as 'King of Kings' within you, O-pen wide the door to-day!

617 His Name is as Ointment poured forth

A.C.

A. CADMAN.

Slowly and worshipfully.

His Name is as ointment poured forth, Je-sus, Je-

- sus, Je - sus, Je - sus, His Name is as ointment poured

forth, His Name is as ointment poured forth.

618   Christ is enough in Sunshine

Arr. by W. G. HATHAWAY.

Christ is e-nough in sun - shine, Christ is enough in dark - ness,

Christ is e-nough He loves you, He is a Friend so true;

When your heart is heavy as you walk life's way, Jesus turns your darkness in-to

glor-ious day: When skies are grey keep trusting, He is a Friend so true.

619   It was just an old, old story

J.I.

Air by J. IRELAND.

Arr. by W. G. HATHAWAY.

It was just an old old sto - ry told o-ver and o-ver to
me, ... How God so loved that He gave His Son to die up-on
Cal - va - ry; . . . It was just an old old sto - ry but
when I be-lieved it true, . . . The peace of God swept over my soul and the
old, old sto-ry was new, (praise God) the old old sto-ry was new.

620 What singing there will be up there

H.M.

Hugh Mitchell.

What singing there will be up there, What singing there will be up there, When face to face with Je - sus we shall stand, And join the heav'nly choir in the bet - ter land. What singing there will be up there, What glo - ry for the saints to share, Oh glo - ry, glo - ry, glo - ry, What sing-ing there will be up there.

621   Lay your Life on the Altar for God

H.M.

HUGH MITCHELL.

Lay your life on the al - tar for God,............ He's call-ing for you to -

- day ;............ Lay your life on the al - tar for God,............ this

mo-ment the Mas-ter o - bey ;............ The fields of the har-vest are white,....

.... And servants are scatter'd and few,............ Lay your life on the

al - tar for God,............ He's call-ing for you, for you............

Elim Choruses, No. 13

622

Out and Out for Jesus.

N.J.C.

Norman J. Clayton.

1. I want to be out and out for Je - sus, Ev -'ry day and ev -'ry hour; I want to be yield-ed to my Sav-iour, And know His mighty pow'r: Liv-ing ev-'ry moment for His glo - ry, Tell-ing ev-'rywhere His wondrous love and grace; I want to be out and out for Je - sus 'Till I see His face.

Let's Talk about Jesus.

H.B. Jr.   HERBERT BUFFUM, Jr.

1. Let's talk a-bout Je - sus, let all the world pro-claim
2. Let's talk a-bout Je - sus, the Bread of Life is He,
3. Let's talk a-bout Je - sus, the Prince of Peace is He,
4. Let's talk a-bout Je - sus, the Rock of A - ges He,

Let's talk a-bout Je - sus, the King of Kings is He,

The Pow'r and Ma - jes - ty   of such a won-drous name,
The Sav-iour of the world,   that Man of Gal - i - lee,
The Great Phy - si - cian too, down thro' all His - to-ry,
The Lamb for sin-ners slain,   that Man of Cal - va-ry,

The Lord of Lords su-preme,........ thro' all e - ter - ni - ty

The Babe of Beth - le - hem,   the Bright and Morn-ing Star,
The Pro-phet, Priest and King, the Might-y God is He,
The Li - ly Pure and white,   the Rose of Shar - on fair,
The Great Im - man - u - el,   the Word of God su-blime,

The Great I AM, The Way,   the Truth, the Life, the Door,

Let's sing His prais - es   near and far.
The well of Liv - ing   Wa - ter free.
The Shep-herd of such   ten - der care.
He is our Bride-groom   so di - vine.

Let's talk about Je - sus more and more.

624   **Christ Meets the Need of Youth.**

H.F.L.

H. F. LANCE, Arr. P. E. RONAN.

Christ meets the need of youth, Christ meets the need of youth, His
ser-vice is full of de - light, There's joy as for Je-sus we fight,
cres e rit.
Pro-claim-ing His great truth, Christ meets the need of youth.

625   **My Lord is Real.**

Old Melody.

Not fast.

My Lord is real, yes, real to me, My Lord is real, yes, real to me.
My soul demands re - al - i - ty, My precious Lord is real to me.

626　　**Some Bright Morning.**

CHARLOTTE G. HOMER.　　　　　　　　　　CHAS. H. GABRIEL.

Some bright morn-ing, Some glad morn-ing, When the sun is shi-ning

in th'e-ter-nal sky; Some bright morn-ing Some glad

morn-ing We shall see the Lord of Har-vest, By and by.

627　　**Touch of Nail Scarred Hand.**

V.B.　　　　　　　　　　　　　　　　　　　VINCENT BENNETT.

rit.

Touch my life, Lord Jesus, with Thy nail scarr'd hand, As for Thee I live and daily take my stand;

May my heart o'erflow, so that all may know, Thou hast touched my life with Thy nail scarr'd hand.

628 **When the Morning Breaks.**

C.S.A.

CHESTER S. ARNT.

When the morn-ing breaks and sha-dows flee a-way, And we

en-ter in-to glo-rious day; There our Sav-iour we'll see, with Him

ev-er to be, When the morn-ing breaks, And shadows flee a-way.

629 **We'll Never say Goodbye.**

J.R.R.

JOHN R. RICE.

We'll never say goodbye in Glo-ry, In the morning o-ver yon-der; We'll

rit.

nev-er say goodbye in Glo-ry, We'll nev-er say goodbye up there.

Joy! Joy! Joy!

N.J.C.

Norman J. Clayton.

Joy, joy, joy came in-to my heart one
Joy, blessed joy of my Sav - iour came in, came
Joy, joy, joy, blessed joy came in, one

day, Joy, joy, joy came
in - to my heart one day, Won-der-ful joy, of my won-der-ful Sav-iour came

in-to my heart to stay: Je - sus sought and found me, Broke the chains that
in to stay, to stay ;

bound me, And joy, joy joy came in-to my heart that day.

631

Pray Your Way Through.

H.L.

Haldor Lillenas.

Pray your way thro'   Pray your way thro'   If you want

vic-to-ry,   Pray your way thro'   Pray your way thro'   Pray your way

thro'.   If you want vic-to-ry,   Pray your way thro'.

632   I am on the Battlefield for my Lord.

SYLVANA BELL and E. V. BANKS.   Arr. by THOMAS A. DORSEY.

I am   on   the bat-tle - field   for my   Lord,   I'm   on   the bat-tle-

- field   for my   Lord ;   And I   prom-ised Him that I   would

serve Him till I   die ;   I'm   on the battle-field   for my   Lord.

633 ## A Day of Coronation.

H.D.L.

HARRY DIXON LOES.

There's a day of cor - o - na - tion, When we'll crown the Sav - iour King of
Kings; By His grace I'll be one of them,
When the ransomed choir the anthem sings: "Glo - ry to God in the
high - est; Praise to the Lamb who was slain"
We shall live in joy e - ter - nal, For the Prince of Peace shall ever reign.

634 ## From the Bottom of my Heart.

H.D.L.

HARRY DIXON LOES.

From the bot-tom of my heart, I can tru - ly say, I have peace and joy to -

-day, Since the blood of Jesus washed all my sins a-way, Praise the

Lord! I am trust-ing, sing-ing, work-ing, watch-ing;

From the bottom of my heart, I can tru-ly say, Praise the Lord!

635 My Sins are Forgiven I Know.

N.J.C.

NORMAN J. CLAYTON.

CHORUS. *a tempo.*

My sins are forgiven, I know, My sins are forgiven I know; Not thro'

works of my own, But thro' Je-sus alone, My sins are for-giv-en I know.

636   Every Promise in the Book is Mine.

Arr. by Paul Spencer Smith.

Ev'ry prom-ise in the Book is mine, Ev'ry chapter, ev'ry verse, ev'ry line, All the blessings of His love di - vine, Ev-'ry promise in the Book is mine.

637   They Came and They were Blest.

C.A.M.

C. Austin Miles.

They came and they were blest, He gave the wea-ry rest, He made the blinded eyes to see, (to see); He fed the hun-gry soul, And made the wounded whole, By the wa-ters of blue Gal - i - lee.

638 Praise Him in the Morning.

Old Melody.   Arr. by W. G. Hathaway.

Praise Him, praise Him, praise Him in the morning, Praise Him in the noontide,

Praise Him, praise Him, praise Him when the sun goes down;

I love the old time singing, shout-ing, I love the old time way.

I love the old time sing-ing, shouting, preaching, praying, I love the old time way, I

talk about my Saviour, ev'rywhere I go, ev'rywhere I go, ev'rywhere I go. I

talk about my Saviour, ev'rywhere I go, bringing joy, joy, joy, to my soul.

Jesus my Saviour.

M.R.

MOLLY RIGBY

Je - sus   my Saviour who died on Mount Cal - va -

- ry, . . .   Paid   my   ran - som and glo - rious - ly

set   me   free . . .   He saves and keeps me from

day   to day;   He's in my heart and He's come to stay,   Then

one   day in the glo - ry, Like Him   I   shall   be.

640

God Shine a Light

M.R.

MOLLY RIGBY.

Adagio. con espress. Prayerfully.

God shine a light in this dark world thro' me, God shine a
light so that oth-ers may see Thy great love re-veal-ing in
Je-sus from Thee, God shine a light, in this dark world thro' me.

641.

Great is Thy Faithfulness.

T. O. CHISHOLM.

WILLIAM M. RUNYAN.

"Great is Thy faithfulness! Great is Thy faith-ful-ness!" Morning by
morn-ing new mer-cies I see; All I have need-ed Thy
rall.
hand hath pro-vid-ed,—"Great is Thy faith-fulness" Lord,un-to me!

642

Jesus, Lord

W. Plowright.

Ron Jones.

Je - sus   Lord   my   a - dored,

Tho who didst suffer on Cal - va-ry,   Shedding Thy life's blood to set me free,

More   like   Thee,   I   would   be,

Thy ho - ly will   in me ful-fil,   Touch me O Lord,   I   plead.

643

Glorious Peace

B. R.

Bruce Rennie.

Moderato.

O! it pass - eth un - der-stand - ing   the

wond - rous peace of God. 'Twas made for

me by Je - sus when He shed His pre - cious

Tranquillo con esp.,

Blood. 'Tis like a riv - er broad and

deep when sun - shine gilds its spray And

as it flow - eth on - ward it gets deep - er

all the way, Yes! all the way!

644

Jesus is the Mighty Saviour.

Tempo di marcia.

Arr. by P. E. RONAN.

Je-sus is the mighty Sav - iour, Loud-ly the ec-hoes ring,
Je-sus is the migh-ty heal - er, Glad-ly the mes-sage bring,
Je-sus is the great bap - ti - zer, Glo-ry hal-le-lu-jah sing,

cres.

And we re - joice for He's our com - ing King.

645

I know Thou art Here.

H. N.

HERMANN NAYLOR.

Andante con moto. ♩=72.

Mine eyes cannot see Thee Lord, but I know Thou art here, To

help and up - hold me, to com - fort and cheer. I'll

I know Thou art Here—*continued*.

praise Thee, I'll praise Thee, For ev - er mine own, And

one day I'll see Thee, And know as I'm known.

646 Every Moment of the Day.

H.D.L.

HARRY DIXON LOES.

Ev - 'ry mo-ment of the day, My Fa-ther cares for

me, Ev'ry moment of the day, My heart from fear is

free He who sees the sparrow fall, will hear my call,

Ev'ry mo-ment of the day God watches o - ver me.

Oh what a Friend is Jesus.

A. R.

ARTHUR RACE.

Oh what a friend is Je - sus, No other friend so

true; He fills my soul with glad - ness,

His peace He gives me too, Je - sus the friend of

sin - ners, His life He gave for me; That all who

trust and o - bey Him shall be saved e - ter - nal - ly.

648

He's the Mighty One.

Arr. by W. G. HATHAWAY.

He's the Mighty One, He's the Ho - ly One, He's the

fair-est of ten thou-sand to my soul; Rose of Sha-ron fair, Bright and

Morn-ing Star, He's the Al - to-geth-er Lovely One to me.

649

Be of Good Cheer.

A.N.

Mrs. A. NEILSON.

Be of good cheer, Be of good cheer, Fear not, 'tis

Je-sus, Fear not, He's near, Be of good cheer,

Be not dis-may'd, Can't you see it's Je-sus, Be not a - fraid.

650 Wonderful Jesus.

A.N.

Mrs. A. Neilson.

Wonderful, wonderful Je - sus, He's a wonderful, wonderful Lord; He's

ta-ken my burden He's answer'd my call, He's a wonder-ful, wonderful Lord.

651 Christ Changes Not.

A.S.H.

Alice S. Heinz.

He's the same to-day as yes-ter-day, He chan-ges not;

He's the same to-day as yes-ter-day, He chang-es not;

Tho' the world may change and kingdoms fall, He's the Rock of A - ges,

All in All, Yes-terday, to-day and for - ev - er, Christ chan-ges not.

652   **Hallelujah! Jesus is Coming Again.**

Arr. by W. G. Hathaway.

Phyllis C. Spiers

Hal-le - lu - jah! Hal-le - lu - jah! Je-sus is coming, is com-ing again,

Hal-le - lu - jah! Hal-le - lu - jah! Je - sus is com-ing a - gain.

653   **Lord, Send the Pentecostal Power.**

E. Walton-Lewsey.

Ivy C. Holloway.

Lord, send the Pen - te - cos - tal pow'r, The pow'r that comes from Thee; The

pow'r that makes the dumb to speak, The pow'r that strengthens me; The

pow'r that raiseth from the grave, That makes the blind to see; The

pow'r to bless, The pow'r to cheer, Oh grant it now to me.

654   **Come now, Saith the Lord**

ISA. 1: 18.

NORMAN J. CLAYTON.

Come now, and let us rea - son to - ge - ther, saith the Lord;

Tho' your sins as scar - let be, They shall be white as snow;

a tempo.

Come now, and let us rea - son to - ge - ther, saith the Lord:

Tho' they be red like crim - son, They shall be as wool.

655   **Just a Little Talk with Jesus.**

Spiritual.

CLEAVANT DERRICKS.

Now let us   Have a little talk with Je - sus,   tell Him all a-bout our

let us

trou-bles   Hear our faint-est cry   an-swer by and by;
He will   and He will

Now when you   Feel a lit-tle pray'r wheel turning,   know a lit-tle fire is
and you

burn-ing.   Find a lit-tle talk with Je-sus makes it right...............
You will   it makes it right.

656
E.W.S.
Prayerfully.

Jesus Thou Saviour Dear.   E. W. STEVENS.

Je - sus Thou Saviour dear, Strengthen my heart, That all my

life, from Thee ne'er shall I   part,   Till that great day shall dawn,

rall.

when Thou shalt come,   And we shall reign with Thee, in our new home.

657 Praise the Lord with Singing.

W. HEBDIGE. W. HEBDIGE. Harmony MRS. SETH SYKES.

Praise the Lord with singing, raise the joy-ful sound, Praise the Lord with
sing - ing, ring the world a - round, Praise the Lord with sing-ing,
till our work is done; Then midst praises ring-ing, hear the glad 'well done'.

658 Under His Shadow.

N.J.C. NORMAN J. CLAYTON.

Un - der His shad - ow there's rest, bles - sed rest,
Safe - ly a - bid - ing where naught can mo - lest;
Tem - pests may rage and the thun - ders may roar, But

here no storm can en - ter For ev - er - more.

659

I Have a Mansion.

I.S.

IRA STAMPHILL (*arr.*)

I have a man - sion just ov - er the hill - top, In that bright

land where we'll nev - er grow old. When I get

yon - der, I'll n v - ermore wan - der, But walk on

streets that are pur - est gold.

660

It's Beyond my Comprehension.

J.M.

Brightly.

JOHN MONTAGUE.

It's beyond my compre-hen-sion, All my Saviour's love for me; Why He
left His home in glo-ry, And He died on Cal-va-ry; By His
grace I'll praise Him al-way And I'll trust Him to the end, For I
know that He will keep me, He's my Sav-iour and my Friend.

661

My Home is in Heaven.

Arr. by W. G. HATHAWAY.

My home is in Hea-ven, just waiting for me; And when I

My Home is in Heaven—*continued*

get there, how happy I'll be. My home is in Hea - ven, the rent is

free, For Je - sus paid it, on Cal - va - ry.

662 ## In the Morning He is Near.

E. WALTON-LEWSEY.   IVY C. HOLLOWAY.

In the morning Christ is with me, At noon He's ve - ry near; At

ev-'ning when the sha-dows fall, He takes a - way all fear; Some-

times I won - der why it is, He is so good to me; But

when I think of Cal - va - ry, That is e-nough for me.

Jesus Said That Whosoever Will.

A.J.P.

ARTHUR J. PANKRATZ.

Je - sus said that who - so - ev - er will, who - so - ev - er will,

who - so - ev - er will; Je - sus said that who - so - ev - er will,

who - so - ev - er will may come. I'm so glad that He in - cluded me,

He in - clud - ed me, He in - clud - ed me; I'm so glad that

He in - clud - ed me When Je - sus said that whoso - ev - er will may come!

Isn't He Wonderful?

Arr. by W. G. HATHAWAY.

Isn't He wonderful, wonderful, wonderful, Isn't He wonderful, wonderful?

Eyes not seen, ears not heard, 'tis re-cord-ed in His word, Isn't He wonderful, wonderful?

665

By and By.

P.C.S.

By and by when the morning comes, And the saints of

God are gather'd home, We will tell the sto-ry how we ov-er-came,

And we'll un-der-stand it bet-ter by and by.

666   He Loves, He Saves, He Keeps, He Satisfies.

WILLIAM M. RUNYAN.   WENDELL P. LOVELESS.

He loves, He saves, He keeps, He satisfies This longing heart of mine; He

fills my life to o - verflowing With His joy and peace di - vine. He

guides, He guards, He watch - es ov - er me, He slumbers not nor sleeps,

For He is my glorious Sav - iour, And He loves, He saves, He keeps.

667   Happiness.

JANUS READE.   J. E. BOURNE.

The lit-tle ways of happiness, are not so hard to find;

They may not lead to starry heights, but to a Sav - iour kind.

He hung up-on a cross for you, He suffer'd, bled, and died;

If you will take Him as your Friend, He'll always be your Guide.

668　　　　　**The Name of Jesus.**

M.K.K.　　　　　　　　　　　　　　　　Miss M. K. KELLER.

The Name of Je - sus lives with -in my heart, It

breathes in - to my spi - rit heal - ing balm; Bids

all my fears and sor - rows to de - part, Oh,

won - drous Name none oth - er brings such calm.

669 His Name is Jesus, and I Love Him so.

E.R.

Esther Rusthoi, *arr.* W. G. Hathaway.

His name is Je - sus His name is Je - sus,

His name is Je - sus, and I love Him so.

How I a - dore Him, Bow down be - fore Him.

His Name is Je - sus, and I love Him so.

Elim Choruses, No. 14

670   **All the Way every Day with Jesus**

W. P. L.

WENDELL P. LOVELESS.

All the way ev'ry day with Je-sus, With Je-sus, with Je-sus, We'll go

all the way ev'-ry day with Je - sus, We'll joy-ful-ly go with Him all the

way   Because His name   is   won-der-ful,   His grace   is

His name

His grace

wonderful, His love   is   wonderful, He's won-der-ful, wonderful, all the way.

His love

67 Since Jesus Took all my Sins Away

R. C. L.

ROBERT C. LOVELESS.

I'm walk-ing a - long a heav-enly road Since Je-sus took

all my sins a - way, And somewhere there rings a heav-enly

song, That brightens my pathway each day. The sins that

bound me, bind me no more, And now I'm bound for

a heavenly shore, And all the darkness of night has turned to

day, Since Je - sus took all my sins a - way.

Not to Sinai

T.W.

T. Woods.

Not to Si - na - i, Not to Si - na - i, But at Zi - on we've ar-rived;

Not a bro - ken law, Not a bro - ken law, But a Sav - iour who's

a - live. We will sing His praise. thro' the com - ing days,

We will talk of Him and His won-drous grace. Not a bro - ken law,

Not a bro - ken law, But a Sav - iour who's a - live!

673

E. A. S.

I Belong to Jesus

ELMER A. SHUMARD.

I belong to Je-sus   He set me free   And He keeps me
set me free

sing-ing   Sweet mel - o - dy,   Fills my life with sun-shine,

what-e'er be - tide,   I belong to Je-sus,   He's by my side.

674

N. J. C.

Down in the Deepest Sea

NORMAN J. CLAYTON.

Down in the depths of the deep-est sea,   Lie all the sins once charged to me,

Buried for time and e - ter - ni - ty,   Down in the deep-est sea.

God's Grace Hath Appeared

W.P.L.

WENDELL P. LOVELESS

For the grace of God that bringeth sal-va-tion, hath ap-pear'd to all men,

Teaching us that, de-ny-ing un-god-li-ness and world-ly lusts, we should live

so-ber-ly, righteously, and godly, in this pres-ent world;
so-ber-ly, righteously,

Look-ing for that blessed hope, looking for that blessed hope, and the glo-ri-

-ous ap-pearing of our Saviour Je-sus Christ, of our Saviour Jesus Christ

676   **Why do I Sing about Jesus**

A.A.K.

ALBERT ALLEN KETCHUM.

Why do I sing a-bout Je - sus? Why is He
pre-cious to me? He is my Lord and my
Sav - iour, Dy-ing! He set me free!

677   **My Hope is in Thee**

AVIS M. CHRISTIANSEN.

GEORGE S. SCHULER.

Won - der - ful Sav - iour, all glo - ry to Thee, In Thee
Won - der - ful, Wonderful Saviour, glo - ry all glory to Thee, In Thee

is sal-va - tion so full and so free; I'll shout forth Thy
full and so free;

WOMEN. MEN.

prais - es thro' all e-ter-ni-ty; My Sav-iour, My Sav-iour

PARTS. *ad lib.* My hope, yes, my hope is in Thee.

My hope is in Thee, My hope, is in Thee.

in Thee

678 There's Music in my Soul

M.D.

MERRILL DUNLOP

There's mu-sic in my soul; My night has chang'd to dawn, Since

rit.

Jesus' blood hath made me whole, My sins are gone, And there is mu-sic in my soul, And

joy be-yond control; There's mu - sic, mu-sic in my soul.

679 **Everlasting Glory Too**

N. J. C.

NORMAN J. CLAYTON.

Ev-er last-ing life, ev-er-lasting home, Ev-er-last-ing glo-ry,

Never-changing love, ne-ver-ending joy And never-failing peace di-vine;

Fine.

D.S. ev-er-last-ing life, ev-er-lasting home, Ev-er-last-ing glo-ry too.

Oh. Je-sus once was slain for us, But ev-er-more He lives, And

to the soul that trusts in Him The Sav-iour free-ly gives His

D.S. 𝄇

680 **I Keep in Touch with Jesus**

MARGARET W. BROWN.

HOWARD L. BROWN.

Brightly.

I keep in touch with Je-sus, And He keeps touch with me; And

so we walk to-geth-er in per-fect har-mo-ny: There's

not a day that pass-es, There's not an hour goes by, But

rit.

that we have sweet fel-low-ship, My pre-cious Lord and I.

681 **Send a Great Revival in my Soul**

B.B.M.

B. B. McKinney

Send a great revival in my soul,........ Send a great revival in my soul,........
in my soul, in my soul,

Let the Holy Spirit come and take control, And send a great revival in my soul........
in my soul.

Sunshine Song

Air by D. HUGHES.
Harmony by JOHN HARWOOD.

D. HUGHES

When you are worried, When you are down, Don't be blue or mope or wear a frown, Je-sus's near to turn your fear in-to sunshine.

Full Surrender

J.C.H.

J. C. HAWKINS

Full sur-ren-der, Full surrender, One hundred per cent for Christ! Be cru-ci-fied, be sanc-ti-fied, One hun-dred per cent for Christ! Let naught remain in heart or brain, Cut ev-'ry rope, let none remain! One hun-dred per cent for Christ!

684 Jesus can Satisfy

N.J.C.

N. J. CLAYTON

Je - sus can sat-is-fy the heart, Glad - ness and peace He can im - part;

Each passing day, All thro' life's way, Je - sus can sat-is-fy the heart.

685 Let me Burn Out for Thee

B. F. H.

BESSIE F. HATCHER

Let me burn out for Thee, dear Lord, Burn and wear out for Thee;

Don't let me rust, or my life be A failure, my God, to Thee.

Use me, and all I have, dear Lord, And get me so close to Thee—That

rit.

I feel the throb Of the great heart of God, Un - til I burn out for Thee.

Copyright, 1929, by Bessie F. Hatcher. International Copyright Secured.

Carry Away a Song

L. F. T.

LAURIE FORBES TAYLOR.

Car-ry a-way a song, Car-ry a-way a song;

Keep God's message of love in your heart As you trav-el a long, (along.)

Tho' the road may be wea - ry, Sing a song that is cheer - y,

Live the hap-pi - ness Je - sus imparts, And car-ry a - way a song.

687   He's a Wonderful Saviour to Me

VIRGIL P. BROCK

BLANCHE KERR BROCK

For He's a won-der-ful Sav-iour to me, (won-der-ful) He's a

won-der-ful Sav-iour to me; (won-derful) I was lost in sin, but

Je-sus took me in: He's a won-der-ful Sav-iour to me.

688 ## Glory Hallelujah!

N. E. B. and LELAND GREEN.

NORAH E. BURNE.

Glo-ry, hal-le-lu-jah! Christ has set me free;

Glo-ry, hal-le-lu-jah! A new life now I see. My

sins are all forgiv'n, I'm on my way to heav'n To live e-ter-nal-ly.

Glo-ry, hal-le-lu-jah! He's com-ing soon for me!

Calvary Covers It All

Mrs. W.G.T.

Mrs. Walter G. Taylor

Cal - va-ry covers it all, My past with its sin and stain; My

guilt and despair Je-sus took on Him there, And Cal-va-ry cov-ers it all.

Wonderful Day of Rejoicing

F. H. Squire

Arrangement by G. R. Klumper

O won-der-ful day of re-joic - ing when Je - sus met with me; And

showed such a wondrous sal-va - tion that brought me lib - er - ty. Each

day as I draw clo-ser to my Lord, His blessings a-bound and my prais-es resound, For there's

no friend like Je-sus my Sa - viour, I'll praise Him o'er and o'er.

691

Go On Going On

W.P.L.

WENDELL P. LOVELESS.

Go on go-ing on, Chris-tian, Go on go-ing on,

Tho' the days are dark and drear - y, There is light a-head, And sure - ly

wait-ing won't be long. Christ, the Saviour's just the same

Yes - ter-day, to-day, for ev - er, Go on go - ing on.

Jesus, My Jesus

A.B.

ALEX BURNS

March time.

Je - sus, my Je - sus; Sa - viour and
Friend............... Je - sus, my Je - sus;
true to the end............... Mine, mine for ev -
er, We'll nev - er part..................... Je -
- sus my Je - sus dwells in my heart.................

693 Out of the Pit

B.K.

BETTY KEPNER.

Up! Up! Out of the pit Je-sus lift - ed me one day;............ Up! Up! Out of the hor - ri - ble pit and the mir - y clay;............ He set my feet on the Rock............ es - tab - lish - ing my way,................ He put a new song in - to my heart; A song that's there to stay................

Looking For Jesus

A.B.

ALEX BURNS

Slow, with expression.

Look-ing for Je - sus; Waiting for His com-ing; Long-ing to see my

Saviour face to face; Serv-ing while wait-ing for that glorious morning;

FINE.

When He shall come to take me Home. Strife all around me, In this world of

dark-ness; What would I do with - out my Saviour's love? I'm but a stran-ger

D.C. al fine.

in this land of sad-ness; I have a Home pre-par'd in Heav'n above. That's why I'm

695

He Gave Himself For Me

A.B.

ALEX BURNS

He gave Himself for me;.......... He gave Himself for me;.......... Up-

rit. *a tempo.*

on the Cross of Cal - va - ry; He gave Himself for me..........

696

Jesus Blessed Saviour

J.M.

JOHN MONTAGUE.

Slow.

p Je-sus bles-sed Sav - iour, Hear us now we pray; As we bow be-

- fore Thee, At the close of day; Bless and keep us ho - ly,

Ev - er in Thy sight, Je-sus blessed Sav-iour, Grant this pray'r to - night.

697

Jesus! My Wonderful Friend

A.B.

ALEX BURNS

Je - - sus! my won-der-ful Friend; Je - -
- sus! on Him I de-pend; He'll nev-er leave me,
nev - er grieve me; Je - - sus! my won-der-ful Friend.

698

My Only Plea

OSWALD J. SMITH.

B. D. ACKLEY.

My on-ly plea, He died for me! Died be-cause He lov'd me long a - go;

He took away my sin, Cleans'd my heart with-in, That is why I love my Saviour so!

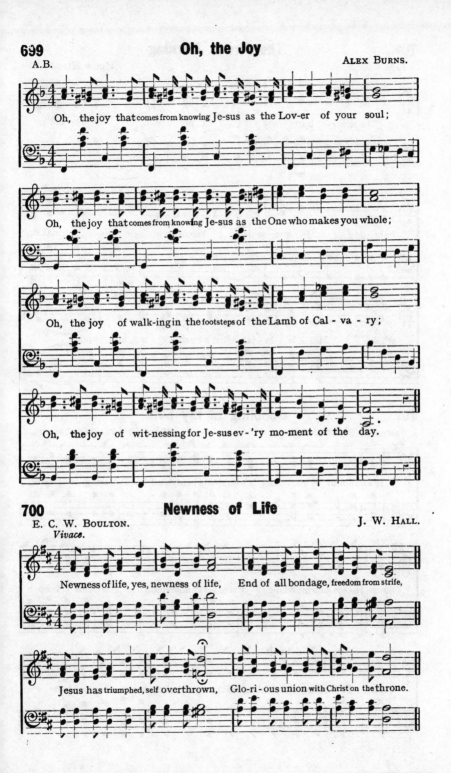

699

A.B.

Oh, the Joy

ALEX BURNS.

Oh, the joy that comes from knowing Je-sus as the Lov-er of your soul;

Oh, the joy that comes from knowing Je-sus as the One who makes you whole;

Oh, the joy of walk-ing in the footsteps of the Lamb of Cal - va - ry;

Oh, the joy of wit-nessing for Je-sus ev - 'ry mo-ment of the day.

700

E. C. W. BOULTON.

Newness of Life

J. W. HALL.

Vivace.

Newness of life, yes, newness of life, End of all bondage, freedom from strife,

Jesus has triumphed, self overthrown, Glo-ri - ous union with Christ on the throne.

701 **The Fire is Burning**

H.M.

HUGH MITCHELL.

The fire is burn-ing in my soul, The fire is burn-ing in my soul; The flame of glo-ry maketh whole, Hal - le - lu - jah! it's burn-ing in my soul.

702 **Bubbling in my Soul**

JAMES P. SULLIVAN.

MILDRED SULLIVAN LACOUR.

It's bubbling, it's bubbling, It's bubbling in my soul, There's singing and laughing, Since Je-sus made me whole. Folks don't understand it, Nor can I keep it quiet, It's bubbling, bubbling, bubbling, bubbling, Bubbling, day and night.

703

A.B.

All I Want is Jesus

ALEX BURNS

All I want is Je - sus; No one else will do; He's a Friend so
faith - ful; Al-ways kind and true; Lov'd me ere I knew Him;
Died to set me free; All I want is Je - sus; Lamb of Cal - va - ry.

704

W. GEORGE.

He's Coming Very Soon

W. GEORGE, *Arr.* GLADYS FRENCH.

Spirited.

He's com-ing ve - ry soon, To ban-ish all the gloom, He's com-ing ve - ry
soon, As vic - tor o'er the tomb, And when with Him in glo - ry His
face we shall be-hold, We'll tell the wondrous sto - ry, The half was never told.

705

Let Go and Let God

J.I.

J. IRELAND. Harmony by W. G. HATHAWAY.

Let go and let God! Lay hold of your bur-den no long - er;

Let go and let God! His grace is sufficient for thee.

Let go and let God! Let Je-sus the Saviour come in. Give

God all the praise, He will bless all your days, If you let go and let God.

706

Just a little Longer

Just a lit-tle long-er, And the trump of God shall sound,

Just a lit-tle long-er, And we'll all be glo-ry bound;

Look a-way to heav-en, Your redemption draw-eth nigh;

Just a lit-tle long-er, And we'll meet Him in the sky.

707

F.M.

A Thankful Heart

FRANCES MORRISON.

Moderato.

To Thee, O Lord, my voice I raise, And from a thank-ful heart, give praise

To Thee, for blessings Thou hast poured Up-on my life, and rich-ly stored

It with such blessings from a-bove, Those deep express-ions of Thy love.

cres.

So let it be, throughout life's days, My lips, my life show forth Thy praise.

Jesus now lives Here

When Sa-tan knocks at my heart's door, and says I'll come in if I may, I'll
say no! no! Jesus now lives here, And there's no room for Satan now in here. So he
turns round and runs a-way.   So he turns round and runs a-way.

709

Let Thy Love fill Me

Mrs. J.C.S.C.   Maori Melody.   *Arr.* by Mrs. J. C. S. Coppin.

p Oh   Lord let Thy love   fill me and reach
through me to Christ - less man;   Thy   com - ing draws
near,   help me to speak   low while I can.

Looking Unto Jesus

F.M. *Con e spirito.*

FRANCES MORRISON.

Keep look - ing un - to Je-sus, Your Sav - iour, Friend and

Guide, And trust in Him at all times,............ For

He is by your side;................... Just lean up - on His

strong arm,........ Though weak-ness be your lot,................ Keep look - ing

un - to Je-sus,............ The One Who changeth not...................

8va................

Joy is Dwelling in my Heart

ALERED SMITH.

Joy is dwelling in my heart, Joy that never will de-part;
my heart, de - part;

Keep-ing all the joy bells ringing, As I journey on my way.
my way.

Hap-pi-ness and joy di - vine, Since I made the Saviour mine
di - vine, He's mine

Now I shout and sing, For Je-sus is my King—O praise His name.
praise His ho - ly name.

I'm Glad I'm a Christian

Arr. by W. G. HATHAWAY.

I'm glad I'm a Chris - tian, I'm trusting the Lord, I'm read-ing the

Bi - ble, believing His Word. The past is for-giv - en, I'm happy and free, A mansion in hea - ven, is waiting for me.

713   When you climb up Sunshine Mountain

A. S. F. HORNE.
Harmony by G. PALMER.

When you climb up Sun-shine Moun-tain, All the air is fresh as Spring; And the birds are ev - er sing - ing, Joyful prai-ses to their King. So why not come and join them, In their sweet and glad re - frain, And climb up Sunshine Moun - tain once a-gain.

Stop ! and Let me tell You

Arr. by W. G. HATHAWAY.

Stop!   and let me tell you What the good Lord's done for   me.

Stop!   and let me tell   you What the good Lord's done for   me, For He has

healed my bo-dy and saved my soul,   bap-tised me and made me whole.

Stop!   and let me tell   you   What the good Lord's done for   me.

715   **Jesus is Alive !**

N. YOUNG

Air by N. YOUNG
Harmony by J. NICHOLSON.

Je -   sus is a-live;   Je -   sus is a-live:

His   is the Blood that ransomed me,   His   is the pow'r that keeps me free;

His ri-sen life is giv'n to me, For Je sus is a-live!

716   I can almost see that City

Rev. Kennedy.

Melody by Rev. Kennedy. U.S.A.
Harmony by W. G. Hathaway.

I can al-most see that Ci - ty Just beyond yon distant hills. The

Ci - ty of my a - bid-ing, When God my Fa-ther wills. So I

press more stead-i - ly on - ward; Soon I shall see the King. I can

ritard.

al - most see that Ci - ty; Some-times I hear the an-gels sing.

Consecration

F.M. *Moderato.*

FRANCES MORRISON.

Just take me to Thy-self Lord, No long-er I'm my own;......... I on-ly want to be Lord, Just Thine, yea Thine a-lone,......... So use me as Thou wilt, Lord, just how, and when, and where......... Thy wis-dom will de-cide, 'Til I've reached the land that's fair.........

8va........

Elim Choruses No.15

718   ## I Fell in Love with Jesus

Alfred B. Smith

I fell in love with Je-sus,...... At the Cross of Cal-va-ry..........

I fell in love with Je-sus,...... And now praise God, I'm free!.....

His grace is like a riv-er........ Flow-ing on e-ter-nal-ly.......

And I know He'll keep me for His own, And some day His face I'll see.....

Everybody Ought to Know

Arr. by W. G. Hathaway

Everybody Ought to Know (*Continued*)

do.......... I love Jesus Hal-le-lu-jah, Jesus smiles and loves me too.

I love Jesus He's my Sav - iour, Je - sus smiles and loves me too.

720 Oh, for a New Anointing!

Joseph Templeton   Hugh Mitchell

Oh, for a new a-noint-ing, Oh, for a heavenly flame,

Oh, for a new a-noint-ing, To glo-ri-fy Thy name!

Oh, for sin and self to cease, Oh, for a sense of in-ward peace;

Oh, for His glo-ry to increase Sav-iour anoint me now.

Don't Worry, Just Trust

Arr. by W. G. Hathaway

Don't worry just trust, be-lieve it you must, He knoweth the way that you take, And

Fine

so as you go, it is heav-en to know, He knoweth the way that you take.

ritard   *D.C.*

All along life's way,   Ev'ry passing day,   Jesus will be there,   Ev'ry burden bear.

722   # Tighten My Grip

M.F.   Mrs. M. Fardell

Tight-en my   grip,   O Lord tight-en my   grip   to the

Hand that was wounded for   me............   In   case I should slip, O Lord

tight-en my grip That my life may be hid-den   in   Thee............

He's a Constant Fount of Joy

H.M.

Hugh Mitchell

He's a constant fount of joy, He's so wonderful! He's so wonderful! He's an

end-less spring of joy, I'm so hap-py in the Sav-iour's love. I can

nev-er tell how much I love Him, I can nev-er tell His love for me, How I

long that oth-er souls might know Him, He's so won-der-ful to me. Sat-is-

fied in His em-ploy, He's so won-der-ful, He's so won-der-ful! He's a

con-stant fount of joy, He's so won-der-ful to my soul.

724

On the White Page

L.S.L.

Lida Shivers Leech

I want my name on the white page, Washed from ev-ry stain of sin;...... I
want my heart pure and ho - ly, That the Lord may dwell with-in.......... I
want my name on the white page,When I stand be-fore my Lord; I
want my robes pure and spot - less, Washed in Je-sus' pre-cious blood......

725

God Can Do Anything

I.F.S.

Ira F. Stanphill

God can do an - y -thing, an - y -thing, an - y -thing, God can do
He can save He can fill just be-lieve that he will God can do

God Can Do Anything (Continued)

an-y-thing I know. an-y-thing I know. Never doubt, always shout,

tho' your vict'ries may be few He's the same and He can do an-y-thing I know.

726 Let the Echoes Ring

A.H.   Archibald Hall

Let the ech-oes ring! Let the ech-oes ring! Let us show to

oth-ers we have cause to shout and sing; Let the ech-oes ring with

Je - sus' prais-es, Let the joy-bells ring in heaven a - bove.

727 His Abiding Love

J. I.

Melody by James Ireland
Harmony by W. G. Hathaway

Slowly and with worship

His a-biding love, Wonderful and free; His amazing tenderness, For a soul like me. His redeeming grace, Pour'd from heav'n above; His eternal constancy, His abiding love.

728 Living for Jesus

T. O. Chisholm

C. Harold Lowden

O Je-sus, Lord and Saviour, I give my-self to Thee; For Thou, in Thy a-tonement, Didst give Thyself for me; I own no other Master, My heart shall be Thy throne; My life I give, henceforth to live, O Christ, for Thee a-lone.

rit. - - - -

Wonderful Story, Sing it Again

J.W.

Jack Ward

Brightly

Won-derful, wonderful, won-der-ful sto-ry Sing it a-gain and a - gain..........

.... Sing of a Saviour who came down from glory, Coming to save sinful men......

..... Thro' faith in His blood I am whiter than snow I'll tell this glad story wher-ev-er I

go. Wonderful, wonderful, wonderful story Sing it a-gain and a - gain..........

Jesus Gave Her Water

Arr. by A.B.S.

Jesus gave her wa-ter that was not from the well, Gave her liv-ing water, and sent her forth to tell; She went away singing, And came back bring-ing Oth-ers for the wa-ter that was not from the well.

731 I Will Sing of the Mercies of the Lord

Arr. by W.G. Hathaway

I will sing of the mercies of the Lord for ever I will sing, I will sing, I will sing of the mercies of the Lord for ever I will sing of the mercies of the Lord.

Fine

With my mouth I will proclaim it, Thy faithfulness, Thy faithfulness, With my

D.S.

mouth I will pro-claim it, Thy faithfulness to all gen-er-a - tions.

732 Christian Business Men's Chorus

F.C.

F. Cunningham

We are Christian Business Men, saved by grace di-vine, Witnessing for Christ our Lord,

rit.

read-y at an-y time, to tell to all that Christ can sat-is-fy, We'll be

faithful to God's word:"Diligent in business— Fervent in spirit— Serving the Lord."

733 Jesus Took my Burden

Arr. by W. G. Hathaway

Je-sus took my burd-en, and He roll'd it in the sea, He roll'd it in the sea, He roll'd it in the sea, And now I am so happy, as hap-py as can be, For Je-sus took my burden, and He roll'd it in the sea.

734 I'm in Love With Jesus

A.N.

Mrs. A. Neilson

I'm in love with Je-sus......... He's the O-n-ly One............ Chief-est of ten thou-sand.......

I'm in Love With Jesus *(Continued)*

Morn - ing star and Sun. Li - ly of the

val-ley The dear soon com - ing King,..........

I'm in love with Je-sus...... His prais-es will I sing......

735   **Only Jesus Satisfies**

Oswald J. Smith   B. D. Ackley

Je-sus! all the world to me,   Je-sus! sat-is-fied in Thee;

Yes, sat-is-fied with

Je-sus! Sav-iour, Friend and Guide,   I am ful-ly sat-is - fied.

Je-sus!

My Lord Knows the Way

S.E.C.

Sidney E. Cox

My Lord knows the way thro' the wil-der-ness, all I have to

do is fol-low. My fol-low. Strength for to-day is mine al-way,

and all I need for to-mor-row. My Lord knows the way

thro' the wil-der-ness, all I have to do is fol-low.

737

His Name is Wonderful

J.S.

James Smith

His name is won-der-ful,..... The mighty God is He; ...... The Coun-sel-

-lor, The Prince of Peace,............ My Sav iour Lord and Christ,....

...The Pearl of Great-est Price....His name is won-der- ful to me.....

738 It's a Sure, Sure Thing

H. D. L.

Harry Dixon Loes

It's a sure, sure thing the song I sing Is not a-bout a vain im-ag-in-

-a-tion; But the song I sing of Christ, my King, Is all a-bout my won-der-ful sal-

-va - tion, Life was once a min-or strain, But now a glad re- frain. It's a

sure, sure thing the song I sing Is all a-bout my won-der-ful sal-va - tion.

One of These Days

Evelyn Baer

*Trumpets

740 Win the Victory

G. B.

G. Bolderson

If the Sav-iour is the One, The on-ly One, that you a-dore; And you
want to win, for Him, the vic-to-ry, Trust in Him, be-cause He loves you as no
oth-er lov'd be-fore; And He wants His child to win the vic-to-
ry! But if you're thinking that you're weaker than the dev-il and you'll fail; Even
tho' you know the Saviour leadeth thee, Just re-member He has promised,
and His word shall e'er prevail: He is with you till you win the vic-to-ry!

741   Glorify Thy Name

J.S.

James Smith
Arr. W.G.H.

Bless Thy Word un-to our hearts and glor-i-fy Thy Name.

Glor-i-fy Thy Name Lord, Glor-i-fy Thy Name.

Bless Thy Word un-to our hearts and glor-i-fy Thy Name.

742   Great is the Lord

A. Thick

G. M. Parkes

Great is the Lord and great-ly to be praised,

Won-der-ful He is in all His ways;

Great is the Lord (*Continued*)

Lov - ing and true, faith - ful to you,

Glo - ry, glo - ry, hal - le - lu - jah, praise ye the Lord!

743   Jesus is Coming Again

M.R.

Molly Rigby

Allegretto

He's com - ing a - gain, He's com - ing a - gain,

Je - sus is com - ing a - gain,.......... His glo - ry I'll see, like

Him I shall be, Yes, Je - sus is coming a - gain...........

744 Keep on Believing

M. Duff

C. M. Booth

Keep on be-liev-ing, Je-sus is near;

Keep on be-liev-ing, There's nothing to fear;

Keep on be-liev-ing, this is the way,

Faith in the night as well as the day.

745 Precious Hiding Place

S. D.

Mrs. S. Danks

Prec-ious hid-ing place, Prec-ious hid-ing place. His

Precious Hiding Place (*Continued*)

smit-ten side my ref-uge, My prec-ious hid-ing place.

746

F. E. R.

The Way

F. E. Robinson

It's the Right-way, It's the Bright-way, It's the Way that leads to ev-er-last-ing Joy. It's the Gate-way, It's the Straight-way, It's the on-ly Way that sinners can em-ploy. It's the High-way, It's the Sky-way, It's the Way that leads to God's e-ter-nal throne. It's the Son Way, It's the One Way, It's the On-ly Way that leads straight home.

cres.

fff

rit.

747   What Can I Bring Thee Saviour?

Lyn Neilson

Leslie Neilson

What can I bring Thee my Saviour,   In re-turn for Thy great love to me,   For re-demption so full and so pre-cious,   By Thy Blood shed on Cal-va-ry's tree?   What can I of-fer Thee Saviour, When the whole of Creation is Thine,   Take my heart, my Life, and my all, dear Lord, To be fash-ioned by Thy Love Di - vine.

748   We Worship Thee

H. J.

Hector Jones

We worship Thee Lamb of Calva-ry, Praise Thy Name for ev-er thro' E-ter-ni - ty.

We Worship Thee *(Continued)*

Thou Lord of Lords at Thy feet we fall, King of Kings we crown Thee as we yield our all.

749   **Jesus is Lord of All**

Len Outhred   David Morgan

O what a joy to be-long to the King, Je-sus is Lord of

all...... Now let this message triumphantly ring, Je-sus is Lord of

all................. Je - sus a-rose and is still on the throne, Ex-

-al - ted a-bove ev'ry power that is known. And soon He is com-ing in

tri-umph for His own, Je - sus is Lord of all..........

My Heart's Rejoicing

S.D.

Mrs. S. Danks

My heart's re - joi - cing I've been set free, My
heart's re - joi - cing in lib - er - ty........... My
Sa - viour died......... on Cal - v'ry's tree, To
par - don a re - bel,...... To par - don me...........

751 God is Moving

God is mov-ing by His Spir-it, Mov-ing o'er all the earth.

God is Moving (Continued)

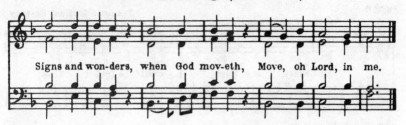

Signs and won-ders, when God mov-eth, Move, oh Lord, in me.

752 Put Your Hand in the Hand of the Lord

R.C.L.

Robert C. Loveless

Put your hand in the hand of the Lord, and step by step He will guide you.

Though the way be dark and drear, You will have your Lord be - side you.

Put your hand in the hand of the Lord, and He will see you thro', Trust in

Him each day, For He knows the way, Put your hand in the hand of the Lord.

753 Thine Alone

J.M.B.

Jeanette McNeal Brissey

Solo, or Voices in Unison

O Christ, my Lord, I would be lost in Thee,

As drops of rain from sum-mer show'rs Are lost with-in the

bound-less sea; Oh, may Thy will my life, my be-ing

own; En-fold me, hold me, till my-self be Thine a - lone.

754 Jesus has Whispered Sweet Peace

A.N.

Mrs. A. Neilson

Je-sus has whis-pered sweet peace to my soul, Je-sus has touched me and

now I am whole Won-der-ful Je - sus, won-der-ful Lord,

Jesus has Whispered Sweet Peace (*Continued*)

Crowned in my heart He is loved and a-dored. Washed in His blood and made

ev-'ry whit whole, Je-sus has whis-pered sweet peace to my soul.

755   Thou Shalt Never Know Defeat

N.Y.

Norman Young. Harmony by W. G. Hathaway

Thou shalt nev-er know de-feat, Christ for thee has won the

day; Thou shalt nev-er know de-feat, He is with thee all the

way. Thou shalt nev-er know de-feat, He will be thy strength and

stay. Thou shalt nev-er know de-feat, On-ly trust Him and o-bey.

756

S.D.

Send Down a Blessing

Mrs. S. Danks

Send down a blessing O Lord today, Send down a blessing to day.........

Turn hearts of stone to flesh for Thine own, To Thy Name the Glo - ry be.........

Sweep thro' the land with re - vi - val Lord, Help us to watch and pray.......That

souls shall be saved, the sick shall be healed and be - liev-ers more ho - ly be.......

757

Love of God, Eternal Love

Amy Carmichael

Jack Ward

Love of God, E - ter-nal Love, Pour Thy Love thro' me.   Noth-ing less than
Love of God, E - ter-nal Love, Sweep my bar-riers down.   Love of God, E-

Love of God, Eternal Love (*Continued*)

Cal-v'ry-Love Do I ask of Thee: Fill me, flood me, o - ver-
-ter - nal Love, Let Thy pow'r be shown. Fill me, flood me, o - ver-

- flow me, Love of God, E - ter-nal Love, Pour Thy Love thro' me.
- flow me, Love of God, E - ter-nal Love, Sweep my bar-riers down.

758   Up in the Blue, Blue Sky

Mrs. W.

Melody by Mrs. Willing
Harmonised

Up in the blue, blue, sky My Sa-viour waits on high, Wait-ing so

pa - tient-ly Watching o'er you and me, Waiting to see us thro', Telling us

what to do, Look up on high and see The won-der of the Lord..........

759

F.M.

My Heart's Yearnings

Frances Morrison

Andante con expressivo

Tis' for Je - sus my heart's yearn-ing, Clos-er to Him I would be, He's my sa - tis-fy-ing Por-tion, He is Ev - 'ry-thing to me. He's the One I love and cher-ish, He's my tru - est, dear-est Friend. I will love and trust Him ev-er, I will serve Him to the end.

760

J.S.

Breathe on Me Spirit of God

James Smith

Breathe on me spirit of God, Breathe on me spi-rit of God,..... Fill my life with the love of Je-sus Breathe on me spirit of God,.....

Spirit of the Lord Descend

E. Walton-Lewsey

Ivy C. Holloway

Spir - it of the Lord, des - cend up - on us now; En-
-due us with Thy migh-ty pow'r while at Thy feet we bow. The
pow'r that fell at Pen-te-cost, we ask of Thee, O Lord; Burn
up the dross send down the fire, Thy gra-cious aid af - ford.

And Again They Say, Hallelujah

Arranged by W. G. Hathaway

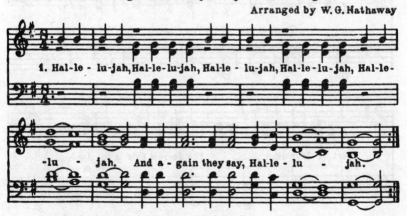

1. Hal-le - lu-jah, Hal-le-lu-jah, Hal-le - lu-jah, Hal-le-lu-jah, Hal-le-
-lu - jah. And a - gain they say, Hal-le - lu - jah.

2. For the Lion of the tribe of Judah hath prevailed
   To loose the seal and to open the Book.

The Dearest Friend

Flora Cartwright

Frances Morrison

I've found a lov - ing Sav - iour,......... Whose lov-ing, loy - al, true,......... When storms of life per-plex me,......... He al-ways sees me through,......... His grace is aye suff-i-cient,..... To meet my ev - 'ry need,............ With all my heart I love Him,......... The dearest Friend in - deed............

Elim Choruses, No. 16

Magnify the Lord with me

Arr. by W. G. HATHAWAY

Mag-ni-fy the Lord with me.......... Bless-ed Man of Cal-va-

-ry; For His grace so rich and free, O, mag-ni-fy the Lord with me.

Mag-ni-fy the Lord with me,......... Bless-ed Man of Cal-va-ry;

Je-sus gives me Lib-er-ty, O, mag-ni-fy the Lord with me.

765 When I think of the Goodness of Jesus

When I think of the Goodness of Jes-us,....When I think of what He's done for

me; My soul crieth out Hal-e-lu-jah,....Praise God for sav-ing me.

766 Kingdoms may Rise

Arr. by W. G. HATHAWAY

Kingdoms may rise, Kingdoms may fall, Nations re-fuse to heed God's call,

But the word of the Lord en-dur-eth for ev-er - more.........

Flowers so fair blooming to-day, Will on the morrow fade away, But the

Kingdoms may Rise *(continued)*

word of the Lord en-dur-eth for ev-er-more........

Put your trust in Jes-us, He will be your Friend;

He a-lone will guide you to your jour-ney's end,

Things that we love last but a day, Heav'n and earth will fade away, But the

word of the Lord en-dur-eth for ev-er-more........

767 In the Secret of Thy Presence

Arr. by W. C. HATHAWAY

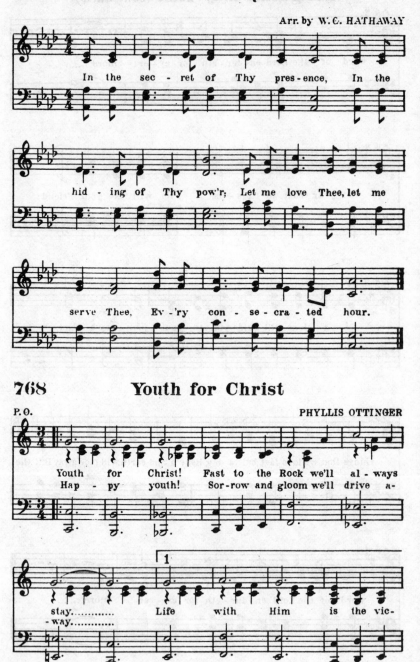

In the sec - ret of Thy pres - ence, In the
hid - ing of Thy pow'r; Let me love Thee, let me
serve Thee, Ev - 'ry con - se - cra - ted hour.

768 Youth for Christ

P. O.

PHYLLIS OTTINGER

Youth for Christ! Fast to the Rock we'll al - ways
Hap - py youth! Sor - row and gloom we'll drive a-

stay............ Life with Him is the vic-
-way............

Youth for Christ (Continued)

-to - rious way............ We'll con-quer sin,

We're bound to win, We are Youth for Christ!

769 God's Love is Wonderful

S.E.C.   S. E. COX

God's love is won-der-ful, God's love is
God's love

won - der - ful,........ Won - der - ful that He should give His

Son to die for me. God's love is won-der-ful.

770 Since I Stopped and Listened to Jesus

F.C.H.

FRANK C. HUSTON

1. Since I stopped, and lis-tened to Je - sus, There's a glad new
2. Won't you stop and lis - ten to Je - sus? O my friend, He's

song in my soul;... Thro' His won-der-ful grace, in His heart I've a place,
call-ing for you;.... If you let Him come in, He will save you from sin,

Since I yield-ed to Je-sus' con-trol........... I'll fol-low wher-e'er He may
And for-ev-er be faith-ful and true.......... He'll give un-to you life e-

lead me, No clouds shall my path-way be - dim,....... I'll love Him and
-ter - nal, And ful-ness of joy all the way....... Ac - cept Him, my

rall. — *ff*

serve Him for-ev - er, I'm so glad that I lis-tened to Him (to Him).
friend, and for - ev - er, You'll be glad that you lis-tened to-day (to-day).

Taste and See

F. M.

FRANCES MORRISON

On - ly taste and see .... that the Lord is

good............ Let the 'Bread of Life'.............. be your

dail - y food..........Thus by feast - ing on Jes-

-us day by day,............. You'll be strength-

-ened and cheered,........ all a - long life's way...........

772 He's Coming! He's Coming!

W.G.H.

W. G. HATHAWAY

He's com-ing! He's com-ing! My Sav-iour from on high;
I'll praise Him. I'll praise Him, For all His love to me;

1

I'll meet Him. I'll greet Him, And join Him in the sky.

D.C.

2

And al-ways think of Cal-va-ry, Throughout e-ter-ni-ty.

773 There's a Precious Hiding Place

Arr. by W.G. HATHAWAY

Worshipfully

There's a pre-cious hid-ing place, In Je-su's side, In Je-su's
side. There's a depth of heav'n-ly grace, In Je-su's side, In Je-su's
side. There's a shel-ter from all sin; From all doubt, from all

There's a Precious Hiding Place *(continued)*

pride. All the world may en-ter in,......Precious place, In Je-sus' side.

774 Cast Your Every Care

N.J.C.

NORMAN J. CLAYTON

Cast your ev-'ry care on Je - sus, Take them all to Him in

prayer, Peace di-vine shall keep your heart, Joys un-known will

God im - part; Rest-ing in the love of Je - sus,

Trust-ing through the sha-dows grim, Days are bright with sun-shine,

Nights are sweet with song, When you cast your ev-'ry care on Him.

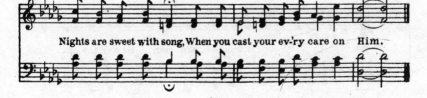

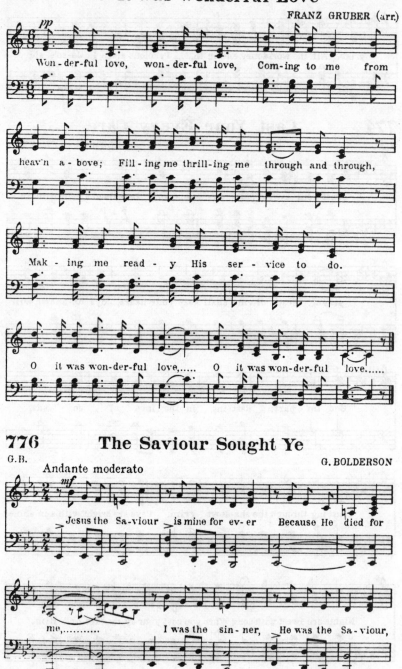

775 O It was wonderful Love

FRANZ GRUBER (arr.)

Won-der-ful love, won-der-ful love, Com-ing to me from
heav'n a-bove; Fill-ing me thrill-ing me through and through,
Mak-ing me read-y His ser-vice to do.
O it was won-der-ful love,..... O it was won-der-ful love......

776 The Saviour Sought Ye

G.B.

G. BOLDERSON

Andante moderato

Jesus the Sa-viour is mine for ev-er Because He died for
me,......... I was the sin-ner, He was the Sa-viour,

He gave His life for me.......... And as I wandered far from my
home, The Saviour sought me sought me a-lone, And since He
found me His arms are round me, That I might nev-er roam.

777 I am the Way, walk thou with Me

R.R.

RUTH ROBINSON
Harmony by Derek Holroyd

I am the Way, walk thou with Me; I am the
Truth, trust Me and see. To give thee life, I died for
thee, And bore thy sins on Cal-va-ry.

778   He is Worthy to be praised

Arr. by W. G. HATHAWAY

He is worth-y to be praised who lift-ed me........ He is

worth-y to be praised who set me free,..... He is worth-y to be

praised who o-pened hea-ven un-to me, He is worth-y to be praised.

779   Jesus will Walk with Me

N.J.C.

NORMAN J. CLAYTON

My Re-deem-er will walk with me, On the waves of life's

trou-bled sea; His stong hand will di-rect the way,

Jesus will Walk with Me (*Continued*)

Lead-ing, pro-tect-ing me day by day: My Re-deem-er is

near to guide, Hold-ing me up o'er the swell-ing tide;

Fear and doubting there need not be, For Jesus will walk with me.....

780   Keep in Tune with Heaven

EDW. HOLT

WENDELL P. LOVELESS

Keep your heart in tune with heav-en; Keep your heart in tune with God;

Read His word and pray each mile a-long the way, Keep your heart in tune with God.

781 **Sing Along**

H.D.L.

HARRY DIXON LOES

Sing a-long life's path-way, With Je-sus in your heart;

Shed a-broad the sun-shine He on-ly can im-part;........Oth-ers

soon will catch the spir-it, That will make the joy-bells start;

Sing a-long life's path-way, With Je-sus in your heart.

782 **Keep Looking to Jesus**

D.L.B.

DOROTHY L. BRAUN

Keep look-ing to Je-sus, The Life, the Truth, the Way;........

Keep Looking to Jesus (Continued)

A - bide in Him ev - er, Our Strength, our Joy, our Stay........

Keep look-ing to Je - sus, Un - til all else grows dim;......

Keep look-ing to Je - sus, And trust - ing Him........

783 I will follow where He leadeth

C. F. W.

C. F. WEIGELE

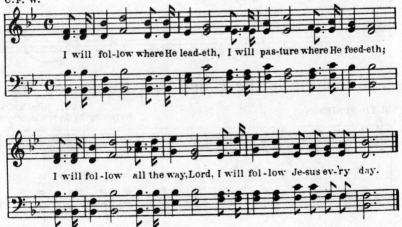

I will fol-low where He lead-eth, I will pas-ture where He feed-eth;

I will fol-low all the way, Lord, I will fol-low Je-sus ev-'ry day.

N.J.C.

NORMAN J. CLAYTON

There is a Guide, Close by my side, One who can keep me from fall-ing,

He's ev-er near, Calming my fear, Faith-ful-ly guarding the way;......

Ten-d'rest love He shows to me, Lead-ing where I can-not see,

Sun-shine or rain, He will sus-tain, Won-der-ful Guide is Je-sus......

785 Thine is the Blood that Ransomed Me

RUTH ROBINSON

RUTH ROBINSON
Harmony by Derek Holroyd

Thine is the blood that ran-somed me, Thine is the

Thine is the Blood that Ransomed Me *(Continued)*

hand that guid - eth me; Mine is the heart that will

glor - i - fy Thee For all Thy won-d'rous love to me.

786   O What A Wonder

R.S.

RALPH SCHURMAN

O what a won-der that Je - sus found me, Out in the dark-ness, no

light could I see, O what a won - der He put His great arm

And won-der of won-ders,

un - der, And won - der of won -ders, He saved ev - en me,

787 **Jesus Has been there too**

A.G.W.S.

A.G. WARREN SMITH

Re-mem-ber when-ev-er you're temp - ted Je-sus has been there, too... From the battle field you're not ex-emp-ted; Jesus has been there, too... Strong op-po-si-tion you're bound to meet; Be oft in prayer at the Mas-ter's feet And as you kneel at the Mer - cy-seat, Je-sus will be there, too......

788 **I will Trust Jesus**

F. M. Allegretto

FRANCES MORRISON

Je - sus my Sav-iour, I'll trust Thee my Friend; For Thou wilt

I will Trust Jesus *(Continued)*

love me right on to the end; Thou in whose keep-ing, I'll

rest all se - cure; For Thou wilt give me the grace to en - dure.

rit. **ff**

789 Nothing Impossible

E. WALTON - LEWSEY

IVY C. HOLLOWAY

Noth-ing shall be im - pos - si - ble to you who be - lieve. This

won-der-ful promise ev-'ry-one may re-ceive. But oh to be - lieve it and

make it your own. 'Tis then, on - ly then, God's pow'r will be shown.

790 **Faith Sees a Way**

F. M.

FRANCES MORRISON

Faith sees a way. Love makes it,......... But, un-be-lief for-sakes it.......

What-e'er you face up-on.... life's track, Nev-er lose heart, nor yet...look back....

But un-to Je - sus, Who will guide And see you through, what-e'er be-tide.

791 **I'm Richer than a Millionaire**

Arr. by W. G. HATHAWAY

I'm rich-er than a mil-lion-aire, Just be-cause He

cares. I'm rich-er than a mil-lion-aire, Just be-cause He

cares. Good-bye pov-er-ty, good-bye des-pair, I'm

I'm Richer than a Millionaire (continued)

go-ing to a mansion He has prom-ised to pre-pare, I'm

rich-er than a mil-lion-aire, Just be-cause He cares.

792   Teach me to Pray

J.E.

JAMES IRELAND
Harmony by W.G.H

Teach me to pray as Je-sus prayed, There in Geth-sem-an-e,

Teach me to walk in low-li-ness, As He walk'd by Gal-i-lee.

Teach me to live as Je-sus lived In all hu-mil-i-ty.

Teach me to love as Je-sus loved, For love has lift-ed me.

793   Have you been down in the Valley

S.D.

Mrs. S. DANKS
Arr. by W. G. HATHAWAY

Have you been down   in   the Val-ley where the sur - ges

roll? Have you been up   on   the moun-tain where the breez-es

blow? Have you been down in death's dark vale   of sor-row and of

woe? O there's lift-ing up in   Je-sus thro' the Crim-son.... Flow.

794   O Saviour Lord, before Thy Cross

E.C.W. BOULTON

J.W. HALL

Andante

O Sav-iour Lord, be-fore Thy Cross, A hum-bled emp-ty soul   I

bow, O take the off-ring that I bring, And seal me with Thy Spi - rit

O Saviour Lord, before Thy Cross *(continued)*

now, E'en tho' it costs in tears and blood, This yearning heart Thy best would

know; Shall less than all Thy al - tar claim, When such a debt I owe.

795   I go along with a Song

W.P.L.   WENDELL P. LOVELESS

I go a-long with a song because the Lord has done so much for

me; He has saved me from sin, Now He lives within my heart, O, praise His Name;

I go a-long with a song be-cause some-day He's com-ing back for

me; Praise the Lord, I am His, and He is mine e-ter-nal-ly.

796 Meet Christ in the Morning

N.M.

NORMAN MABLE

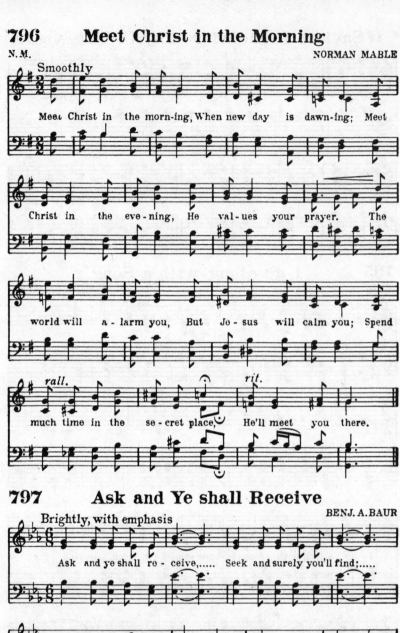

Smoothly

Meet Christ in the morn-ing, When new day is dawn-ing; Meet

Christ in the eve-ning, He val-ues your prayer. The

world will a-larm you, But Je-sus will calm you; Spend

rall.   *rit.*

much time in the se-cret place, He'll meet you there.

797 Ask and Ye shall Receive

BENJ. A. BAUR

Brightly, with emphasis

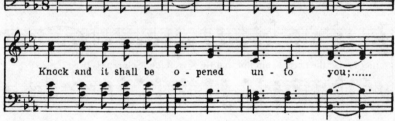

Ask and ye shall re-ceive,..... Seek and surely you'll find;.....

Knock and it shall be o-pened un-to you;......

Ask and Ye shall Receive (continued)

Ask and ye shall re - ceive, Seek and sure-ly you'll find;.....

Knock and it shall be o - pened un - to you.......

798 **He found me with a Burden**

ANON.

W. G. HATHAWAY

He found me with a bur-den,..... And He lift - ed it....from me;.....

He found me bound and fet- tered.... and gave me lib - er - ty,..........

He found me in the darkness,... And He made the sun.... to shine...... Can you

won- der why.....I love Him,..... And call Him Friend of mine......

799 We Thank Thee, Lord

Arr. by W. G. HATHAWAY

We...thank Thee, Lord for this our food, God is Love!... God is Love!

Much more be-cause of Je-sus' blood, God is Love!.... God is Love!

These mercies bless and grant that we May feast in Pa-ra-dise with Thee,

May feast in Pa-ra-dise with Thee. God is Love!.... God is Love!

800 Oh, Thou Sun of my Soul

E.P.

ELEANOR PANKOW

Oh, Thou sun of my soul.......... Oh, Thou day-star on

Oh, Thou Sun of my Soul *(continued)*

high;........ Al - pha, O - me - ga, the sweet Rose of

Shar - on,...... Je - sus Thou art.... to me................

801 After the Daybreak

B.B.H.

BARBARA B. HART

Af-ter the day-break, what glo-ry 'twill be   Ev - er   in

Heav-en with Je-sus to be;   Loved ones will greet me and

welcome me home   Af-ter the day-break,   Nev-er to roam.

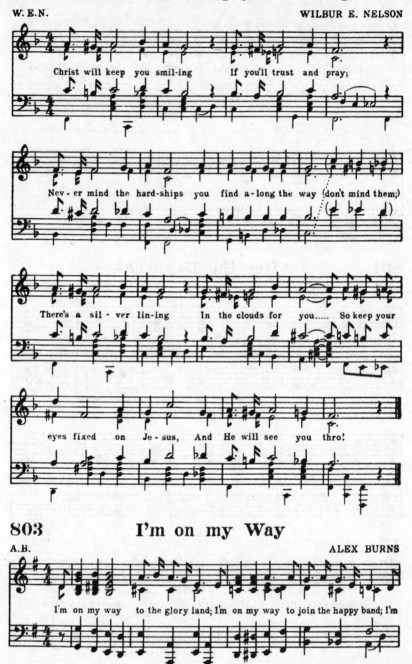

802 Christt will Keep you Smiling

W. E. N.

WILBUR E. NELSON

Christ will keep you smil-ing   If you'll trust and pray;

Nev-er mind the hard-ships you find a-long the way (don't mind them;)

There's a sil-ver lin-ing   In the clouds for you..... So keep your

eyes fixed   on   Je-sus, And He will see   you thro!

803 I'm on my Way

A.B.

ALEX BURNS

I'm on my way   to the glory land; I'm on my way to join the happy band; I'm

I'm on my Way (continued)

on my way; My! it's simply grand I'm on my way* to glo-ry.

*Various effects as "clap hands" may be used here.

804   **Happy Today**

S.W.G.   STANTON W. GAVITT

Happy today with my sins washed away, I'm re-joic-ing and praising the Lord;

Hap-py to-day with my sins washed away, I'm be-liev-ing God's ho-ly word.

Come and believe and sal-va-tion receive, you'll be re-joic-ing too;   You'll be

happy today with your sins washed away, Rejoicing and praising the Lord.

805 He Touched me and made me Whole

T. S.

THOMAS SULLIVAN

He touched me and thus made me whole(made me whole), Bring-ing

com-fort and rest to my soul(to my soul); O glad hap-py day, all my

sins washed a-way! For He touched me and thus made me whole(made me whole).

806 Pray till the Light breaks Through

ANNETTE DENNSTEDT

B. D. ACKLEY

Pray till the light breaks through Pray till the light breaks through; There is
breaks through.

strength and pow'r For the trying hour, If you pray till the light breaks through.

807   Joy of my Longing Heart

R.W. O.

RICHARD W. OLIVER

Joy of my long-ing heart,...... Light of my dark-est
day................. Je-sus to me Thou art.................
     dark-est day,
All that I need al - way.............. Now that I walk with Thee,
Ev - er my soul can see.................. Light from Thy face,......
     my soul can see......
Joy in Thy grace, Joy of my long-ing heart.......

In a Manger slept a Stranger

H.E.F

HELEN E. FROMM

1. In a man-ger, slept a Stran-ger,'Neath the star-ry
2. Seek the Stran-ger in the man-ger, Greet Him, Je-sus,

heav-ens bright, Breez-es blow-ing, gen-tly blow-ing
Lord, at birth, Bow be-fore Him and a-dore Him,

Out in the si-lence of.... the night, An-gels sing-ing.
Bringing thy gifts, O ye men of earth, Give Him glo-ry,

ti-dings bring-ing,"Peace on earth,good-will to men," Shep-herds
tell the sto-ry, How the world's Re-deem-er came, Come, re-

seek Him, wise men greet Him, At Beth-le-hem. ....
-joic-ing, prais-es voic-ing To Je-sus' Name.........

Elim Choruses, No. 17

809 There's a Rainbow Shining Somewhere

Anne Campbell   B. D. Ackley

There's a rain-bow shin-ing somewhere, There's a light across the skies; There's a rain-bow shin-ing somewhere, Like a gleam from Par-a-dise; Tho' to-day the clouds are drift-ing Far a-cross the storm-y sea, There's a rain-bow shin-ing some-where That will some day shine for me.

810

The Height of His Love

W.G.H.

W. Gardner-Hunter

Allegro

Could we measure the height of His love___ 'Twould be higher than Heaven a-

love;___ The Sav-iour's de-vo-tion was deep-er than o-ce-an, Such

1
marvellous, marvellous love;___
marvellous love;

2
marvellous, marvellous love.___
marvellous love.

811

Be Still, My Heart

M. Craig

Melody by M. Craig
Harmony by T. E. Francis

Be still, my heart, and know that He is God; Go, cast on

Him thine ev-'ry hea-vy load And find in Him thy

812 Over the Sunset Mountains

J.W.P.

John W. Peterson

O-ver the sunset moun - tains, Someday I'll soft - ly go;___
Toiling will all be end - ed, Shadows will flee a - way;___

In - to the arms of Je - sus, He who has loved me so.___
Sorrow will be for-got - ten Oh, what a wonderful day!___

CHORUS

O - ver the sun-set moun - tains Hea - ven a-waits for me,___

O - ver the sun-set moun - tains, Je-sus my Saviour I'll see.___

813 Trust In The Lord

J.D.W.F.

June D.W. Fardell

When you think there's none to care, Trust in the Lord!

He can ans-wer ev-'ry prayer, Trust in the Lord!

If temp-ta-tions threaten you, If you've lost the peace you knew,

rit.

Turn to Him, He'll see you through, Trust in the Lord!

814 I Will Praise My Saviour

D.N.

Dorothy Niles

I will praise my precious Saviour, I'll ex-tol His love-ly Name, For He

gave His life on Cal-v'ry, Bearing there all my sin and shame. I'll

I Will Praise My Saviour (*Continued*)

sing a-loud His praises, Till I reach yon heav'nly shore. Then I'll

join my hal le - lu - jahs, with ten thousand thousand more.

815
G.D.

It Is Wonderful

Gertrude Diehl

It is won-der-ful, so won-der-ful, that Je - sus died for

me; It is won-der-ful, so won-der-ful, from sin He set me

free. It is won-der-ful, so won-der-ful, He's com-ing back for

me; My Je-sus, my Sa-viour, is won-der-ful to me.

816 This Is Where My Joy Is Found

Arr. by P. Ronan

This is where my joy is found- in Je - sus. This is where my
heart has found a home;_____ This is where my soul has found a
re-fuge dear and sweet Rest-ing at my dear Re-deem-er's feet.

817 Beyond Compare

A.H. *Ad libitum*

Archd. Hall

Be-yond com-pare, the love that Jesus has for me.____ Be-yond com-
-pare, it lasts for all eterni - ty.____ What joy 'twill be if I can help some others
share___ The One I've found, be-yond com - pare._____

818 Love of God come sweeping o'er my heart

W.G.H.

W. G. Hathaway

Vivaciously

Sweep-ing through, pre-cious Lord, sweep-ing through,

Filling all my life in ev-'ry part; Sweeping through, precious Lord, sweeping

ritard - - - - -

through. Love of God come sweeping o'er my heart.

(Male voices) sweeping o'er my heart.

819 More and More

Arr. by W. G. Hathaway

Prayerfully, not too fast

More and more,— I want to mag-ni-fy Thy name; More and

more,— I want to spread abroad Thy fame. More and more,— O make my

life a liv-ing flame; Melt my heart, precious Lord, more and more.

820 He is despised, But He is on the Throne

Cyril P. Davies
Arr. by A. E. A. Hayward

C.P.D.

He is des-pised, and still by men re-ject-ed; He is des-pised, al-tho' He wears a crown:— He is des-pised, the King of Kings in Glo-ry; He is despised, but He is on the Throne.

821 Take Me Back

A.H.   Archd. Hall

Take me back, o'er that barren track, Show me where my Saviour shed His blood. Melt my heart, fer-vent love im-part,

As I see that pre-cious clean-sing flood
pre-cious cleansing flood.

822 I'm Abiding in Canaan Land!

Avis Burgeson Haldor Lillenas

I'm a - biding in Canaan Land! _____ I'm a-biding in Canaan
in Canaan Land!

Land! Since He washed my sins away, It is glo-ry all the way;
in Canaan Land!

I'm a-biding in Canaan Land! ___ All my sins have been forgiv'n,
Canaan Land!

And I'm on my way to heav'n; I'm a-bid-ing in Ca-naan Land!

823 Wonderful Love

W.G.H.

W. Gardner Hunter

Wonderful, wonderful, wonderful love, Love which brought Jesus from
Heaven a-bove; Down from the heights to the depths Je-sus came,
Lift-ing me up to the heights, praise His name; Wonderful, wonderful,
wonder-ful love, Love which brought Jesus from Hea-ven a-bove;
Lord of my life I shall own Him For such wonderful, wonderful love.

824 There's a Work for Jesus

Elsie Duncanvale

Wm. T. Meyer

Work for Je - sus, day by day; Serve Him ev - er,
fal-ter nev-er; Christ o - bey. Yield Him ser - vice
loy-al true; There's a work for Je-sus none but you can do.

825 God's Love is Wonderful

S.E.C.

S. E. Cox

God's love   is wonderful, God's love   is wonderful! Wonderful that

(God's love)   (God's love)

He should give His Son to die for me; God's love   is wonder-ful!

(God's love)

826 By Thy Body and Blood

W.J.C.

W. J. Clemnell

Worshipfully

pp Lord, by Thy Bo-dy and Blood, we in thankfulness, At Thy com-

mand, to Thy ta-ble draw near; Worshipping Thee in the

beau-ty of ho-li-ness: Lord, in Thy presence, Thy Voice we would hear.

827 I love my Jesus, O yes I do

D.J.T.

D. J. Thomas
A.T.S.C.

Joyously

I love my Je-sus, O yes I do,— For He first loved me, I

know 'tis true;— and now I mean to be through and through a

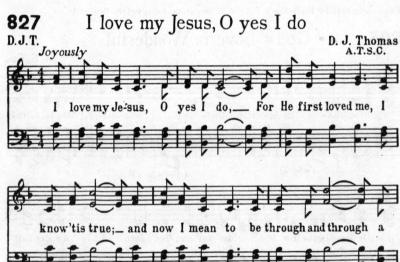

I love my Jesus, O yes I do (*Continued*)

true dis-ci-ple; will you be, too?— He is the fair-est of

all to me,— The tru-est friend I will ev-er see:— He

left the Glory to set me free, and with Him someday I'll ev-er be.—

828 Jesus, Thou art my dearest Friend

M. Jameson

M. Brown

Je-sus, Je-sus, Thou art my dear-est Friend; Guide— and

keep me faithful to the end.— Help me to praise Thee whatever may be-

fall.— And may Thou be crowned King of my soul, my life, my all.—

829 We Love and Adore Thee

W. J. C.

W. J. Clemnell

We love and a-dore Thee, our wonderful, wonderful Sa - viour; We
bow down be-fore Thee and joy-ful-ly sing "Halle - lu - jah!"
Lord, keep us near Thee, Let not our faith ev-er wa - ver; We

rall.

love and a-dore Thee, Christ Je-sus, the Lord of Light.

830 Workers Together

F. M.

Frances Morrison

Con spirito

mf We are workers to-geth-er, To-geth-er with the Lord; We are

Workers Together (Continued)

work-ers to-geth-er, He tells us in His Word. Just keep

on do-ing your part, and glad-ly I'll do mine, So that

oth-ers may no-tice how bright our lights do shine.

831 It's A Wonderful Thing

Arr. by W. G. Hathaway

It's a won-der-ful thing, a ve-ry won-der-ful thing, To be

saved from sin, and have Christ within; To be made a joint heir with

Je-sus, my Lord. It's a won-der-ful, won-der-ful thing.

832 Wide Is The Gate

A.S.C.

A. S. Coney

Wide is the gate and broad is the way, That leads to des-truc-tion, pain and loss; We each must choose, our life to gain or lose, The way of the world or the way of the cross. Straight is the gate and narrow is the way Lead-ing to life and joys a-bove; Enter that gate be-fore it is too late, Walk in God's way of light and love.

833 Going On With Jesus

A.H.

Archd. Hall

Are you feeling weary with your life? Does the world de-

press you with its strife? Go-ing on with Je-sus is the

happiest thing I know; He will make your joy o'er-flow.

834 Take Time in the Morning to Pray

Flora Cartwright

Frances Morrison

Allegretto

mf Take time in the morn-ing to pray,— Ask Je-sus to

guide you all day:— The way will be bright-er, though dark be the

sky, Your load will grow lighter, if Je-sus is nigh; He'll give you a

cresc.   *f*   *dim. e rall.*

song as you journey a-long, So take time in the morning to pray.—

I Am Determined

I am determined to hold out to the end; Je-sus is with me, on

Him I can de-pend, And I know I have sal-va-tion, for I

feel it in my soul; I am det-er-mined to hold out to the end.

836 None Like Jesus

F.M.

Frances Morrison

Poco Andante

mf

There is no earthly friend so true, Nor yet a love like His for you; There's

cresc. rit. a tempo e dim.

none to cheer and help you through the path of life, like Je - sus.

837 In The Glory-Land

W.S.

Warren Smith

In the Glo-ry-land, With the God of love, One day we shall dwell a-bove; In that land of light There will be no night, O the joys of the Glo-ry-land! Je-sus died that we might en-ter in; He has wash'd a-way our sin. Saved by grace We shall see His love-ly face, For we'll be in the Glo-ry-land!

838 In the Dawning of the Morning

Rev. A. H. Ackley

B. D. Ackley

In the dawn-ing of the morn-ing I shall see Him, In the radiant glory of eternal day; How my heart will shout and sing, When I see my blessed King! In the dawning of the morning I shall see Him.

rall.

839 Sweep Over My Soul

Arr. by W. G. Hathaway

Sweep ov-er my soul, sweep ov-er my soul, Sweet Spir-it, sweep ov-er my soul. My rest is com-plete, While I lie at His feet. Sweet Spir-it, sweep ov-er my soul.

840 Cheer Up!

Warren Smith

Brightly

Don't be downhearted; Cheer up! Cheer up! For Jesus is on the Throne, And

rall. *a tempo*

He will supply ev'ry need from on high; Cheer up! Cheer up! Cheer up!

841 His Love Is Wonderful

W.M.F. and D.W.

W. M. Foote and D. Wakeman

Allegro

His love is won-der-ful, so mar-vel-lous and true;

His love is wonderful, so marvellous and true. At His feet I

hum-bly fall, and yield to Him my life, my all. His love is

rall.

won-der-ful, so ten-der and so true. (Yes, and so true.)

842 Have You A Saviour?

Chas. Justice and W. Rogers   Chas. Justice, arr. W. Rogers

FEMALE VOICES

mf Have you a Saviour like this Saviour of mine? Have you a friend so true as my Friend divine? Ev-er He walks beside me. Keeps me whate'er betide me; Have you a friend like mine?

MALE VOICES

f I have a Saviour and I know He is mine! I have a Friend so dear, He's my Friend divine! Ever He walks beside me. Keeps me whate'er betide me; I know this Friend is mine.

ALL *Slower*

ff We have a Saviour, and we know it is true!

Have You A Saviour? *(Continued)*

Sunbeams of grace and glory come shining thro'; Goodbye to sin and sadness

Welcome to peace and gladness, Fresh as the morn-ing dew!

843 Singing His Praise

Avis B. Christiansen Arthur W. McKee

Sing His praise, the King of Glo-ry, Let all earth His pow'r proclaim;

Just and righteous are His mandates, True and ho-ly is His name.

Let all na-tions laud and mag-ni-fy, Ev-'ry tongue confess and

glo-ri-fy Christ, the Lord of earth, and sea, and sky, For - ev - er - more.

844 Jesus Won My Heart

Rev. Alfred Barratt D.D.

Harry Dixon Loes

Je-sus won my heart,— Je-sus won my heart; By His love so
He won my heart, He won my heart;

full and free, And the grace He gave to me. Je-sus won my heart,—
He won my

Je-sus won my heart;— By His love so full and free, Jesus won my heart.
heart, He won my heart;

ad lib.

Copyright 1924 by Edwin Young.

845 Cleanse me of all my Sin

D.J.T.

D. J. Thomas A.T.S.C.

Humbly and prayerfully

Cleanse me of all my in - i - qui-ty, Purge me of se-cret sin and dross;

Have mercy, Lord, and with great pi-ty, Draw me with love to Calv'ry's Cross.

846 Jesus Rolls the Clouds Away

H.L. Haldor Lillenas

Je-sus rolls the clouds a-way, Je-sus
turns my night to day; I'm walk-ing in the sun-light since His
love came shin-ing thro', And He rolled the clouds a-way.

847 I Will Follow Thee

R.M. Roosevelt Miller

I will fol-low Thee, dear Lord, I will fol-low Thee;
Whi-ther Thou go-est, dear Lord I'll go, I will fol-low Thee.

848 How Can I Be Lonely?

H.L.

Haldor Lillenas

How can I be lone-ly When I've Je-sus on-ly

To be my com-pan-ion and un-failing guide? Why should I be weary,

rit.

Or my path seem dreary, When He's walk-ing by my side?

849 Breaking through the Clouds

P.S.K.

Phillip S. Kerr

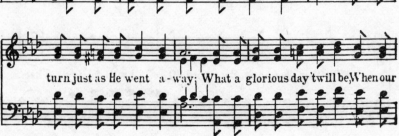

He'll come break-ing through the clouds some-day; He'll re-

turn just as He went a-way; What a glorious day 'twill be, When our

Breaking through the Clouds (Continued)

Saviour's face we see; He'll come breaking through the clouds someday.

someday

850 **Since God Loves Me**

A.H.A.

A. H. Ackley

Since God loves me,——The world is resplendent with gladness; My

God loves me,

soul is free,—— No long-er I wan-der in sad-ness; Since

is free,

God loves me,—— To turn from His love would be mad-ness. The

God loves me,

joy of the morning my life is a-dorning, Since God loves me.——

851 No name has meant so much to me

Oscar C. Eliason   Alfred B. Smith

My heart is stirred whene'er I think of Je-sus, That bless-ed Name which sets the cap-tive free;— The on-ly Name thro'which I find sal - va-tion, No name on earth has meant so much to me.—

852 I Love Thee, Lord

Mrs. S.D.   Melody by Mrs. S. Danks
Harmonised by W. G. Hathaway

I love Thee, Lord, I love Thee, Lord; Let Thy name for-ev-er be En-graved up-on my heart. Let my love forev-er be Engraved upon Thy heart.

853 The Pathway of Life

Anon

P. E. Ronan

'Tis such a nar-row path-way, Yet there's room e-nough for two; There's room to walk with Je-sus, And for Him to walk with you; You would lose Him on the broad-way, The crowd would press be-tween, And on-ly in the narrow path The heart on Him can lean.

854 He's The One I Love

N. B. V.

N. B. Vandall

He's the One I love,____ He's the One I love.____ Fair-er is He than the li-ly to me; He's the One I love.____

855 Have You Heard of Jesus?

D.J.T.

D. J. Thomas A.T.S.C.

Have you heard of Je - sus and His wond'rous love? How He left the splendour

in the heav'n a - bove? He came down to save us from our guilt and

shame; Now we're free for - ev - er, Glo - ry to His name!

856 Make my Life Like a Melody

Arr. by P. E. Ronan

Brightly

Make my life to be (Oh glo-ry) like a mel - o - dy, Ev - er telling out the

message of the Cross; Cross. With Jesus in my heart, no discord can a - rise, for

He can make the saddest note to harmonise; Make my life to be (Oh glory)

like a mel-o-dy, Ev-er tell-ing out the message of the Cross.

857 Counting Blessings

George W. D'Vys

Chas. H. Gabriel

Are you count-ing up your bless-ings all a-long your way? Don't you

see the golden sunbeams all a-round you play? It will help to scatter shadows,

It will drive the clouds away, If you count your many blessings as you go.

I'm an Heir of God

Mrs. W. G. T.

Mrs. Walter G. Taylor

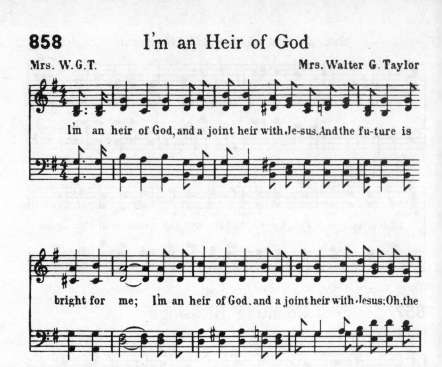

I'm an heir of God, and a joint heir with Je-sus, And the fu-ture is

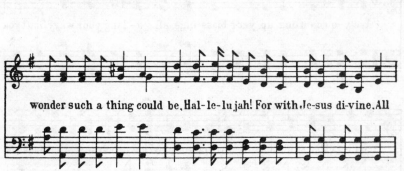

bright for me; I'm an heir of God, and a joint heir with Jesus; Oh, the

wonder such a thing could be, Hal-le-lu jah! For with Je-sus di-vine, All

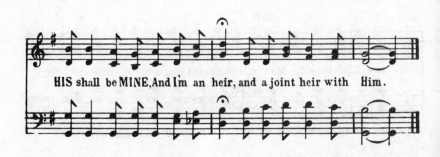

HIS shall be MINE, And I'm an heir, and a joint heir with Him.

Elim Choruses No.18

859

Down Deep In My Heart

O.A.L.
and J.H.

O. A. Lambert
& Johnnie Hope

Moderato

I've got the love of Je-sus down in my heart; down in my heart, down in my heart. I know the love of Je-sus will not de-part, for He's liv-ing Down Deep In My Heart.

860 He Rose Triumphantly

Oswald J. Smith

B. D. Ackley

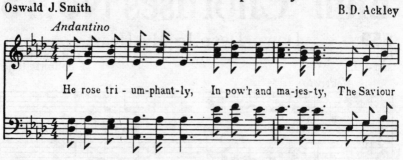

He rose tri - um-phant-ly, In pow'r and ma-jes-ty, The Saviour

rose no more to die;_____ O let us now pro-claim

The glo-ry of His name, And tell to all, He lives to - day._____

861 Let the Dew of Heaven fall on me

Introduced by F. Lloyd Smith

Arr. by W. G. Hathaway

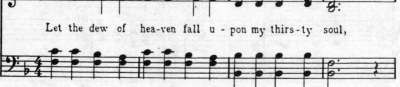

Let the dew of hea-ven fall u - pon my thirs-ty soul,

Let the Dew of Heaven fall on me *(Continued)*

Let the dew of hea-ven fall on me. Bles-sed Ho-ly Spi-rit come and

take con - trol; Let the dew of hea-ven fall on me.

862 I've Lost My Load!

G.C.

Grace Clement

I've lost my load, I've been for-giv - en, I'm on the

road that leads to Hea-ven, and all day long this song rings

out it's me-lo-dy, I've lost my load, my heart is free!

Saved to the Uttermost

Frances Morrison

Tempo di Marcia

He is ab-le to save to the ut-ter-most, All that come un-to God by Him, He is ab-le to lift from the gut-ter-most, All that come un-to God by Him. Though you may be dead in sin, He can give you life with-in, So just come and be saved to the ut-ter-most, On-ly come un-to God by Him.

864 I'll Tell You Why

A.W.

A. Winch

I'll tell you why___ I have a song to sing since
I found the Lord, He loos-ened ev-'ry fet-ter and
un-tied ev-'ry chord.___ I'll tell you why___ this me-lo-
-dy I sing is with me night and day, 'Twas the
song that Je-sus gave me when He washed my sins a-way.___

865 What Shall I Give Thee, Master?

H.W.G.

Homer W. Grimes

Je-sus, my Lord and Sa-viour, Thou hast giv'n all for me;

Thou didst leave Thy home a-bove to die on Cal-va-ry.

What shall I give Thee, Mas-ter? Thou hast giv'n all for me;

Not just a part or half of my heart, I will give all to Thee.

866 I Want That Kind of Blessing

Words and Music E.S. Ufford

Arr. for John T. Benson Pub. Co.

I want, I want that kind of bless-ing, That
want that kind

I Want That Kind of Blessing *(Continued)*

saves and keeps, and sa-tis-fies the soul; I want, I want that
yes,

full sal - va-tion Till bil-lows of hea-ven o'er me roll.

867   My Father Watches Over Me

Rev. W. C. Martin   Chas. H. Gabriel

I trust in God, I know He cares for me,_____ On mountain
He cares for me,   On

bleak   or on the stormy sea;_____ Tho' billows roll,_____ He keeps
mountain bleak or__ on the sea, the stormy sea;   tho' billows roll, He

my

soul,_____ My heav'nly Fa-ther watches o - ver me._____
keeps my soul,

rit.

868 Oh Blessed Holy Spirit

V. E.

Vep Ellis

Oh Bles-sed Ho-ly Spi-rit__ Cleansing through and through

O'er my tongue is flood-ing like a ri-ver ev-er new. A

lan-guage hea-ven hear-eth,__ though to earth un-known

Sweet com-mu-nion, Ho-ly u-nion, God and His own.

869 There's a Great Change in Me

Anon.

Arr. by W.G. Hathaway

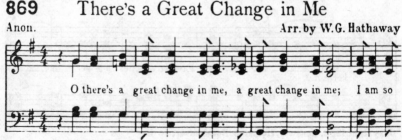

O there's a great change in me, a great change in me; I am so

There's a Great Change in Me (Continued)

hap-py, I am so free. He brought me out of dark-ness in-to

mar-vel-lous light, O, O, O, there's a great change in me.

870 Like the Rolling Sea

G.C.

Grace Clement

Like the rolling sea, sweeping over me comes the wondrous love of Je - sus,

Bearing me u-pon the might-y wave, from the heart of Him who died to save,

Sweeping me a-long, thrilling me with song, filling me with endless peace

Far beyond all measure is the love of Je-sus, wondrous love that cannot cease.

871 That's What He Did for Me

G.R.

Gloria Roe

Play as if ⅜ time

Loved me, bought me, saved me, cleansed me, That's what He did for me. _____ He bore sins, shame gave me His name, That's what He did for me! _____ God so loved me, gave His Son _____ Now that I be-lieve life for me has be-gun! _____ Cleansed me from wrong, gave me this

That's What He Did for Me *(Continued)*

song, That's what He did for me!

872 Jesus, my Lord, has lifted me

R.M.B.   Ruth M. Bailey

Je-sus, my Lord, has lif-ted me,
Now all the day His praise I'll sing,

Out of my sin and mi-se-ry,
Round the whole world His glo-ry ring,

He gave His
Un-to my

life to ran-som me,   Praise His Ho-ly
Lord my all I

Name.   bring, Praise His Ho-ly   Name.

873 Just Kneel at the Foot of the Cross

J. F.

Joe Fudge

Just kneel____ at the foot of the cross,____ Just kneel____

____ at the foot of the cross.____ You'll find all your heart-aches and

trou-bles are lost, When you kneel at the foot of the cross.____

874 Who Can Compare?

F. M.

Frances Morrison

Andante

Who can com-pare with Je-sus my Sa-viour? What can com-

cresc.

-pare with His love for me? In His sweet Pres-ence is

Who Can Compare? (Continued)
dim.

joy with-out measure, On-ly a fore-taste of "Hea-ven to be."

875
A.E.S.

Send the Power

Melody by A. E. Stringer
Harmony by P. E. Ronan

Send the pow'r u-pon Thy people now Lord, Send it in the old time

way, O-pen Hea-ven now Lord, Send a migh-ty show'r Lord,

Let the Spi-rit come to - day, Clo-ven tongues of fire send down u-

-pon us, Burn-ing up the dross and tin, Cleanse our hearts from sin Lord,

Make us pure with-in Lord, Let the Ho-ly Ghost come in.

876 I felt the Hand of the Lord one day

G.C.

Grace Clement

I felt the Hand of the Lord one day, lift-ing me out of the mi-ry clay,

placing my feet on the King's highway, I felt the Hand of the Lord! He keeps His

Hand on me for bless-ing and to help me on the road. I

I'm trav-'ling on with my Lord each day, safe 'neath the Hand of God!

877 Expect a Miracle

V.E.

Vep Ellis

Ex-pect a mi-ra-cle ev-'ry day, Ex-pect a mi-ra-cle when you pray; If

you ex-pect it God will find a way, To per-form a mi-ra-cle for you each day.

878

A.E.K.

Great Was His Love

A. E. Kelly

Je-sus was bruised and wound - ed, Slain on the cru - el tree; Smit-ten of God, the Fa - ther, My Ran-som thus to be;__ I was the one He died for, From sin to set me free;__ Je-sus was bruised and wound - ed, Great was His love for me.__

879 'Twas a Great Salvation

G.C.

Grace Clement

'Twas a great sal-va-tion Je-sus gave to me, E-ver-last-ing life and li-ber-ty, and a glorious future for e-ter-ni-ty, Oh! 'tis a great sal-va-tion.

Ev-'ry promise in His Word is mine! End-less glo-ries on my pathway shine!

I'm so hap-py with my Lord Di-vine, Oh! 'tis a great sal-va-tion!

880 He Sitteth a King Forever

A.W.

A. Winch

He sit-teth a King for-e-ver,— He sit-teth a King to-day;— He hold-eth the reins for e-ver,— He hold-eth the reins to-day.— My

He Sitteth a King Forever (*Continued*)

times, my times are in His hands, His pro - mi-ses shall sure-ly

stand; He sit-teth a King for - e - ver,— He sit-teth a King to - day.

881 In a coming day

F. D. Byatt

Harmony by A. E. A. Hayward

In a com-ing day we'll meet the King of Grace. In a

we'll meet the King of Grace.

coming day we'll look u-pon His face,— We shall meet to part no more, on that

happy Golden Shore, In a coming day we'll meet the King of Grace.

we'll meet the King of Grace

882 I am satisfied with Jesus

E.W.

E. Williams

I— am sa-tis-fied with Je-sus, I have won-d'rous joy and peace with-in. He— has pur-chas'd my re-demp-tion, and He's cleans'd my heart from sin.— Oh— the won-der of sal-va-tion that my bless-ed Lord should come to die! I will ne-ver cease to praise Him for the might-y love that made Him come to save a sin-ner such as I.—

883 He is so Wonderful

G.C.

Grace Clem t

Slow

He is so won-der-ful, He is so won-der-ful, Je-sus my

He is so Wonderful (Continued)

Sa-viour is all things to me, He saves and sat-is-fies, My ev-'ry need supplies, on Him my soul re-lies eter-nal-ly.

884 He made the stars to shine

A.H.

Archd. Hall

Con brio

He made the stars to shine, He made the roll-ing sea, He made the moun-tains high. and He made me But And He made me this is why I love Him, For me He bled and died, The Lord of all cre-a-tion, Be-came the Cru-ci-fied.

885 I'd like to put my hand in Thine

J. F.

J. Fudge

I'd like to put my hand in Thine, dear Lord, Like to put my
like to put my trust in Thee, dear Lord, Like to put my

hand in Thine, dear Lord, My life to live my all to give, To
trust in Thee, dear Lord, My days to spend my way to wend, I'd

1. trust and to o-bey each pass-ing day. I'd
like to put my

2. hand in Thine.

886 Tell me more of Jesus

Harry Dixon Loes

Alfred B. Smith

Tell me more of Je-sus and of hea - ven, Tell me

more of Je-sus and His love; Tell me how He's com-ing soon to

take us, To e - ver dwell with Him in heav'n a - bove.

887 To Him

H.W.G.

Homer. W. Grimes

In a thousand ways, I would sing His praise Thro' the endless days, to Him!

Faster

By His life I live, I would gladly give All I am and have, to Him, to Him,

a tempo — **rit.**

In a thousand ways, I would sing His praise Thro' the endless days, to Him!

888 Pray without ceasing

E.W.

E. Williams

"Pray with-out ceas-ing," thus saith the Lord, He will not

fail you, He's pledged His Word. On-ly be-lieve and you'll

find Him true, Pray with-out ceas-ing, He'll ans-wer you.

889

G.C.

To Him that is Able

Grace Clement

To Him that is a - ble to keep you from fall - ing, To Him whose dear voice is so ten - der-ly call - ing, To Him who can save you from ru - in ap--pall-ing, Oh come with your bur-dens just now.

890

F.D.Byatt

Jesus my Saviour

Harmony by A.E.A. Hayward

Je - sus my Sa - viour, dear-er than all to me, Sweet rose of Sha - ron, man of Cal - va-ry.

Draw me still clo - ser to Thy lov - ing breast,___

For in Thy pre - sence, my soul is blest.___

891 I Will Never Leave Thee

A.E.K.

A. E. Kelly

Allegretto

I will ne - ver leave thee, Tho' clouds ob - scure thy way___

Neither will I for - sake thee, How - e - ver dark thy day.___ My

eye shall e - ver guide thee; My right hand shall up - hold thee; In

tri - umph I will bring thee to E - ter - nal Day.___

892 I Was Far Away

G.C.

Grace Clement

I was far a-way, just a wand'ring sheep, from the fold of God a-stray,

'Till my blessed Lord came to rescue me, oh it was a hap-py day! and now I'm

looking for His coming, working for His kingdom, living for His glory, day by day

Walking in His footsteps, happy to be near Him, in this 'Hal-le-lu-jah Way.'

893 Lord make us One

(As Sung at the World Pentecostal Conference in Paris, 1949)

Arr. by W.G. Hathaway

1. Lord make us one,   Lord make us one,   Lord make us one ev'ry-where
2. One in love di-vine,   One in love di-vine,   One in love di-vine ev'ry-where
3. One in the Holy Ghost, One in the Holy Ghost, One in the Holy Ghost ev'ry-where
4. One in fel-low-ship,   One in fel-low-ship,   One in fel-low-ship ev'ry-where

Lord make us One (*Continued*)

Lord make us one, Lord make us one, Lord make us one ev'ry-where.
One in love di-vine, One in love di-vine, One in love di-vine ev'ry-where.
One in the Holy Ghost, One in the Holy Ghost, One in the Holy Ghost ev'ry-where.
One in fel-low-ship, One in fel-low-ship, One in fel-low-ship ev'ry-where.

894 I'll Sing of My Redeemer

V.E.

Vep Ellis

I'll sing—— of my Re-deemer, of His—— a-mazing grace, And

I'll sing   wondrous grace

when—— my spi-rit sing-eth,'tis re-veal'd His matchless face, and when my

and when

eyes be-hold His glo-ry—— o-ver on that gold-en shore, I'll

gold-en shore,

ne-ver preach or pray a-gain, But I will sing—— for e-ver-more

I will sing

895 That Beautiful Name

Jean Perry

Mabel Johnston Camp

That beau-ti-ful Name, That beau-ti-ful Name, From sin has

rit.   *cresc.*

pow'r to free us! That beau-ti-ful Name, That

ad lib

won-der-ful Name. That match-less Name is Je - sus!

896 Make His Praise Glorious

C. H. M.

Mrs. C. H. Morris

Make His praise glo-ri-ous, Sa - viour vic-to-ri-ous,

Through - out the world be His great name a-

Be His ho - ly name a-

897 But This I Know

C. Austin Miles

Clarence Kohlmann

-dored— Make His praise glo-ri-ous,
-dored, O praise ye the Lord! praise ye the Lord!

Sa - viour vic-to - ri-ous; Let ev-'ry-
praise ye the Lord! praise ye the Lord! Let ev'ry-thing that hath

thing that hath breath praise the Lord.
breath, ev-'ry-thing that hath breath praise the Lord.

But this one thing I know; That, when the crim-son flow Dropp'd to the

earth be-low, it fell on me. My eyes were opened wide, I saw Him

rit.

cru-ci-fied, And knew for me He died on Cal-va - ry.

898 Thank You for Life, Father

Anon.

E. R. Greenwood

Thank you for life, Fa-ther, Thank you for love; Thank you for
won-der-ful things from a - bove. Thank you for Je - sus on
Cal - va - ry's tree; Thank you for sav-ing a sin-ner like me.

899 Those who seek Me early

Pamela Fox

J. W. Arden

"Those who seek Me ear-ly, They shall sure-ly find," This promise I have
claimed and made it ful - ly mine; O help me day by day to

walk Thy wondrous way, and show to all 'round me, Lord that I am Thine.

900 Look Away to Calvary

Julia H. Johnston   Frank C. Huston

Look a-way to Cal-va-ry! Look a-way to Cal-va-ry!

There be-hold the Sa-viour dy-ing On the cru-el cross for thee.

ff Look a-way to Cal-va-ry! Look a-way to Cal-va-ry!

f *p* It was there He died to save thee; Look a-way to Cal-va-ry!

901

Move with God

V.E.

Vep Ellis

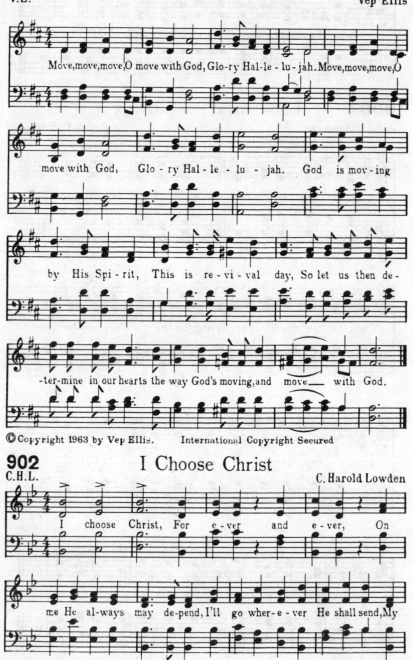

Move, move, move, O move with God, Glo-ry Hal-le - lu - jah. Move, move, move, O move with God, Glo-ry Hal - le - lu - jah. God is mov-ing by His Spi - rit, This is re-vi-val day, So let us then de--ter-mine in our hearts the way God's moving, and move___ with God.

902

I Choose Christ

C.H.L.

C. Harold Lowden

I choose Christ, For e - ver and e - ver, On me He al-ways may de-pend, I'll go wher-e-ver He shall send, My

rit. *a tempo*

life in His blest ser-vice spend, For I choose Christ.

903
A.S.

It's in My Heart

Arthur Slater

It's in my heart _____ this me-lo - dy of love di-
it's in my heart

-vine It's in my heart _____ Since I am His and He is
it's in my heart

mine _____ It's in my heart _____ How can I
yes He is mine   it's in my heart

help but sing and shine _____ It's in my

heart _____ It's in my heart.
it's in my heart   it's in my heart.

He's Alive!

E.W.

E. Williams

He's a-live, He's a-live, He's a-live for e-ver-more,
He's a-live, He's a-live, He's a-live for e-ver-more,

Je-sus is ri-sen from the dead.
Now He's become our Living Head.

Death no longer hath dominion, Satan's

pow'r is bro-ken down, He hath tri-umph'd, Hal-le-lu-jah, and He

wears the Vic-tor's crown. He's a-live, He's a-live, He's a-

-live for e-ver-more, Je - sus is ri-sen from the dead.